The Dail· Proj~~ι

Download the official Daily Trainer app in the Apple Store and Google Play.

Coming Early 2019

Become a Member of DailyTrainerOnline.com – the Future of Fitness Education and Certifications

Daily Trainer, LLC 2201 N Street NW, Washington D.C. 20037: Suite 609

Day by Day

The Personal Trainer's Blueprint to Achieving Ultimate Success

By Kevin Mullins, CSCS

PUBLISHING &
ENTERTAINMENT

Forward Focus Companies LLC

Library of Congress Cataloging-in-Publication Data

Mullins, Kevin, 1988

Day by Day, A Personal Trainer's Blueprint to Achieving Ultimate
Success/ Kevin Mullins – 1st ed.

IBSN: 978-0-578-41792-9

Publisher Number: 1915059

Published in the United States by Future Minds Publishing and
Entertainment, a division of Forward Focus Companies, LLC

1250 Connecticut Ave NW, Washington D.C. 20036 Suite 700

www.futuremindspub.com

Want to publish your book?
FM publishing is looking for individuals looking to advance the
human mind, body, and spirit. Contact Kevin@Futuremindspub.com

Edited by: Cara Sunberg

Design by: Meridith Piazza

Foreword by: Jon Goodman

First Edition

To the those who give it their all, no matter the cost

Table of Contents

Foreword by Jonathan Goodman

I've published more than a thousand articles and seven books. Conservatively, you could say I've been responsible for more than a million value-laden, career-exploding words for fit pros. As a result, I've been privy to a lot of good advice, and a lot that's not so good.

I'll start this foreword by telling you how to identify bad advice.

Bad advice tells you what you think, not how to think. Instead of explaining how to approach a situation and empowering you to make an intelligent decision, bad advice takes the easy route and gives you a step-by-step process.

Bad advice typically comes from fly-by-night sources— men and women who claim success with no evidence to back it up. There's no body of work. No clients whose lives have been transformed. They seem to have come from nowhere, and will soon drift back into obscurity.

There's a reason why Kevin Mullins is one of the most frequently published contributors on my website, the Personal Trainer Development Center. With more than 20,000 client sessions, the dude has put in the work. And it shows.

Truth is, he undersold this book. It's not just a collection of 365 tips. No. It's a collection of 365 golden nuggets of wisdom—wisdom he can only have gleaned from experience.

Take the nugget that starts the book on January 1: Every time you're with a client, you're being watched by curious onlookers, so you'd better put your best

Day by Day

foot forward. Seems obvious, right? But only some-body who's spent a lot of time on the floor understands how difficult it is, day-in and day-out, to maintain this awareness. The January 1 entry is a reminder that the smallest things, done consistently well over years, make the biggest impact.

Other nuggets are just flat-out good advice for simplifying your day-to-day work, helping you avoid headaches you never knew you had. A good example is the suggestion on July 5 to take an extra minute before and after a con-sultation to make sure you send a well-organized email. A poorly structured message opens a time-wasting black hole of needless back-and-forth with the client, as any experienced trainer will attest. Kevin's advice reminds you how simple it is to avoid this trap.

With all this said, my favorite section is the entire month of November. Very little in the fitness industry can be stated in absolute terms, but a lot of information is sold that way. The resulting misinformation and deceit can be hard to sift through, even for the most seasoned pros. I urge you to pay special attention to that material.

I also ask you to trust a guy who's published more than a million words for fit pros when he says that you've stumbled on a real gem here. I'm happy Kevin wrote this book, and I'm excited that you're taking the time to read it.

-Jonathan Goodman

Founder, Personal Trainer Development Center (thePTDC.com) and OnlineTrainer.com

Day by Day

Day by Day

Introduction

The fact that you are holding this book shows that you want to improve yourself and your career. Your commitment to your own growth will help you better drive your clients toward results, your business toward success, and your reputation as an industry leader.

The best in any business, in any pursuit, are the ones who invest their time, energy, and finances into growing themselves. The best investment strategy will always be your own development. Even in the best financial markets it can be hard to match the rate of return that comes with acquiring or refining your skills, increasing your rates, and earning more per hour.

The personal training career is a unique one in that your education pursuits can correlate directly to the rates you can charge, the opportunities that will come your way, and the reputation you'll begin to earn. When you get better, your clients get better, and in turn so does your business.

So here you are, ready to get better, and ready to dive in. You'll feel an urge to sit down and read this book cover-to-cover like most other books. Your desire to get better right now will tempt you to try to do it all at once. Fight that urge and allow yourself the opportunity to maximize your learning by breaking this book down into daily segments.

Each tip is a carefully selected anecdote collected from a decade of fitness experience at a high level. They are the culmination of thousands of hours of labor, education, experience, and contemplation. Each day is designed to progress your thinking, challenge your beliefs, and ultimately elevate you and your career to the next level.

Day by Day

You'll notice these tips focus on a different theme each month, thus allowing you to dive down the rabbit hole of each subject for an extended period. This organization lends itself to better retention of information—a key part of what makes this book worth your investment. The monthly "umbrellas" allow you to isolate one element of your practice for an entire month.

Everyone is coming to this book, and the Daily Trainer platform, for a different reason. Some will be eager to learn tricks of the trade for business practice and client retention. Others will want to review kinesiology and physiology while discovering new methods for challenging clients. Then there are those of you who are open to anything, so long as you find yourself improving.

Each day provides you with an opportunity to load a thought into your head and put it to practice; each month an opportunity to solidify your stance and skills on a subject; and each year, you'll revisit the book to ensure that you are still minding the small details.

The Daily Trainer is here to elevate you as a personal trainer, sure, but there are tips in here that also improve your skillset as a person, a fitness enthusiast, and a thinker. Everything in this book is the result of the successes and failures of me, its writer. Each tip has been reviewed by a team of coaches, editors, and fitness leaders who agree: these will elevate your career.

You'll probably find a tip or two that you don't agree with. It'd be disappointing if that didn't happen, to be honest. With three hundred and sixty-six unique tips, there is bound to be something that makes you scream bullshit. You can't win em' all, right?

Fight that urge to dismiss what you read and instead ask yourself how it might be true. It is often in the area where we have the most conviction that we need the most growth. Our bias blinds us from evolution.

Day by Day

Other tips will make you sit back and say, "Duh, that's obvious." Remember that not all knowledge is shared and that what you know isn't necessarily known by others. Besides, sometimes seeing something you know written in different words is the best way to learn it forever.

This book is also part of a greater operation. The Daily Trainer platform includes an app that is available in the Apple Store and Google Play.

Our website, DailyTrainerOnline.com, (coming early 2019) will become home to the future of personal training education. We aim to deliver the best video content from the top coaches in a format that makes actual learning take place. Our videos will be entertaining and easy to digest while still delivering the best, and most factual, information possible.

You'll soon call Daily Trainer home for staying certified, meeting other professionals, and advancing your career as a personal trainer, coach, nutritionist, physical therapist, or fitness personality.

Lastly, if you have a great tip, course idea, or feedback, please email us at help@dailytraineronline.com. If we love your idea, you'll get credit on all platforms.

With that said, let's start the tips. Happy learning!

Day by Day

Day by Day

January

Professionalism

"We spend January 1 walking through our lives, room by room, drawing up a list of work to be done, cracks to be patched. Maybe this year, to balance the list, we ought to walk through the rooms of our lives... not looking for flaws, but for potential."

—*Ellen Goodman*

"Once you realize that you're in something that you've always wanted, and you don't want to lose it, you behave differently. And that means the integrity, the professionalism, and knowing what's right from wrong and still making choices that you probably wouldn't have made."

—*Paul Anka*

January 1st

Someone is always watching you. Whether you are with a client, conducting your own workout, or hanging out with your fellow trainers in between sessions, there is a high probability that someone is looking at you.

Picture yourself on the gym floor working with your current client. There are people on the treadmills and ellipticals while others lift weights. At some point, everyone's eyes will find their way to you and your client.

What will they see?

Will you be engaged with your client as though they are your top priority, or are you on your phone? Does that client look like they are being coached to do things right, or are you simply knocking out another hour of your day?

You control what others think of you more than you know. Fine-tune the details of your practice to elevate your professionalism. In turn, more people will notice just how in-tune you are with your clients, and your business will boom.

January 2nd

Life happens, but being early for a session should be normal. Investing the extra effort to be waiting for your client is one of the most professional things you can do.

The personal training field charges a specific amount of money for a specific amount of time. This must never be lost on the personal trainer.

Picture how your client feels when they are toiling away on a treadmill or wandering around aimlessly for this trainer they've paid for. Imagine this person already dreads the gym and wishes they weren't there in the first place.

And then you come strolling up five minutes late into an hour-long session. How do you think this will be perceived by this client?

Honor your clients' time and commitment by ensuring you are always available and ready before they are (especially in those early AM sessions). Their session begins the second they arrive to train and not a moment later.

Pro Tip: Sell 55-minute sessions if back-to-back clients cause problems in your day. No one will miss those five minutes if you give them your all during the fifty-five you promised.

January 3ʳᵈ

*A trainer's schedule is their paycheck. Highlight your
hours of availability so clients, prospects, and membership
coordinators at your gym are aware. Manage your schedule
weekly to avoid silly mistakes that could cost you money.*

A poorly managed schedule is a sure-fire way to make
your career rocky and uncertain.

Envision every week with 168 grid lines that can be filled,
with 24 per day over the course of 7 days. First, scratch
out your time off and the hours that gym is closed. Next,
note each hour of your day already allocated to clients,
program design, answering emails, and any other
duties. Now, you can account for personal time, like
your workouts and meals.

Everything left over can be spent on anything you feel is
necessary for your growth or for entertainment.

Mismanaging your schedule can lead to embarrassing
and damaging moments. Double-booking or missing
sessions shoulder never happen. Nor should showing up
sweaty and smelly or still chewing your lunch. Manage
your professional schedule – it is literally your business.

January 4th

Being a personal trainer is a license to wear gym clothes all day and be paid for it. However, take the time to ask yourself if you are presenting yourself professionally. You may want to add your own flare, highlight your body, or simply be comfortable, but remember, no matter what you wear at work, it is still a uniform.

A personal trainer has the freedom to wear a variety of clothing styles to work. Unlike a lawyer who must rock the standard suit and tie, a trainer could sleep in their work attire.

But this isn't a license to dress down to the point where someone might question whether you are working or working out. Save your flare for the moments when you're doing your own thing on your own time.

A trainer should blend into the scenery during their sessions while the client, and the exercises they are performing, demand the attention.

There are always exceptions to every rule (just look at Mark Fisher Fitness in New York City), but black bottoms with a single-colored, sleeved shirt is the most professional look on the job. At the very least it is never wrong, even if it isn't as fun.

January 5th

It may seem normal, but do your best to maintain a barrier between your clients and your personal life regarding social media. A culture of oversharing can lead to a stifled professional relationship. Creating a separate account for your brand is advisable.

Social media has altered the fabric of human interaction. No longer do we need to call each other to catch up on the happenings of the week or reminisce on years past.

It's all right there on our accounts where we willingly share our lives with the public.

And it doesn't matter if your weekends are filled with parties in the city or taking your children to a local park. Keeping a barrier between your professional and personal life is always advisable. You don't want your clients feeling as though they can "friend" their way out of their commitment to you as a trainer and coach.

That doesn't mean you can't share parts of your private life with clients that you trust and vice versa. Instead, today's tip simply encourages you to filter who gets access to your personal life and to avoid sharing everything you do with everyone who follows you.

January 6th

Remember names. Many great professionals have been hindered on their path to success because they couldn't take the time to nail the most basic social grace: learning someone's name. Beyond knowing your client's names, take the time to memorize the names of members you see every day. This will show the quality of your character.

Knowing someone's name is akin to having a golden ticket to their good side. Think about how special you feel when you are greeted by name at your favorite spot.

Treat all people at your fitness facility with this same grace, whether they pay you or not. This accomplishes two things:

- It increases the amount of people who know your name and know you in a positive light.
- It demonstrates that you aren't a cold business person when you speak with those who will likely never train with you.
- It develops your social skills, expands your network, and makes your job more fun.

Remember, it costs you nothing to be thoughtful and even less to be nice.

January 7th

*Build your business without infringing on other trainers'
clients. Even handing out your business card to someone
is poor form if they are already training with someone else,
especially in a commercial gym setting.*

Building a successful personal training business is no
easy feat. You must convince people that you are worth
the investment of their time and money without giving
up too much of your own.

There are also other trainers doing the same thing
around you. You might feel you need to compete with
them, so much so that you would approach clients who
already made their choice.

But realize this: no one wins when you stoop this low. If
you are a better coach, then the clients themselves will
eventually notice and approach you. Never approach
another trainer's clientele and pitch your services. In
the end, they'll wonder why you have the time to pitch
them if you really are better.

The best at anything can market themselves through
action alone. Be the "bigger" coach.

January 8th

Develop unique programs for every client you train. Each person, no matter how common their goal may be, presents an individualized set of abilities, previous experiences, complications, and motivations. It is poor professionalism to prescribe the same workout for every client that comes your way.

Fitness is not a one-size-fits-all sort of business and never should be. Sure, there are group exercise classes and workouts in every monthly magazine, but a personal trainer must go above this threshold.

Being a great trainer doesn't mean writing down a bunch of exercises in the morning and running them on repeat until your day is over. It means making every program unique to the individual you are training.

Always consider the past, present, and future of your client. Where were they, where are they, and where do they want to go?

This is the ultimate role of a *personal* trainer.

January 9ᵗʰ

Always document the work your clients perform in a session. This allows for you to make logical progressions over time as your client adapts to your program. Documentation also provides the legal backing in the event of an accident or dispute with a client.

You are responsible for the health and well-being of your clients during the hours that they are with you. To protect yourself legally, you must maintain an active record of what you did and didn't do in a training session.

From a programming perspective, it's only possible to progress a client if you are tracking past performances. What your client did last week should impact the exercises you select today, or the load, or the volume, or any other factor of fitness.

Lastly, from a sales perspective it's great to be able to sit down and show a client the path of their progression with actual data instead of recollecting memories.

Keep records. Every aspect of your business requires it.

January 10th

Personal training must begin with an in-depth assessment of a client's status, abilities, and needs. Utilizing a standard PAR-Q is a great start, but including movement assessments and detail-seeking questions is critical to uncovering a client's real motivation and needs.

A client is a living, breathing person with a history that must be discovered and understood prior to embarking on a personal training journey.

The best trainers always look to learn as much about their clients as possible before prescribing exercises. Even seemingly minor injuries could cause massive adaptations up or down the kinetic chain that impair their movement or lead to compensations.

The assessment extends into the physiological realm as well. How do they view exercise? How have they been coached? Do they have a support system around them or are they operating on their own?

Every great program starts with an assessment.

January 11th

There is more value in a well-worded follow-up email than there is in a sleek sales pitch at the end of a complimentary session. Sending a communication that summarizes your interactions and presents a solution to the client's needs proves you are a true professional capable of delivering more than expected.

No one likes to be sold. It's an uncomfortable feeling to be in front of a salesperson while they're pushing all the options onto you.

Your client could love everything about you and your training but be uncomfortable with your sales tactics. Avoid this by sending a detailed email that includes your pricing, a glimpse at the program you'll have them on, and answers to the questions they might have.

If you deliver exceptional service, are upfront and honest about pricing and session rules, and are qualified to do what you say you'll do, then you'll have no issues building a brand that avoids forced sales pitches.

Provide information for their decision-making process and be ready to go when they return.

January 12th

A 1-1 training session should be just that. It is important to prioritize your client above all others during the hour for which they are paying you. A great coach understands that the client has an expectation to be treated with absolute attention during a training session. Therefore, keep your interactions with other individuals, including fellow coaches, to a minimum.

Your client is paying you for an hour of your coaching, attention, and friendship. It is important to honor the value of their money and time by emphasizing them throughout the hour.

This doesn't mean you have to stand like a statue and avoid interaction with others around you, but it does mean you should be only coaching your paying client, never on your phone or eating a meal, and always attentive to them while they are moving.

A session is not the time to hand out business cards, reminisce on your weekend with fellow trainers, or say hello to the good-looking person across the way. Train your client and stay focused on their needs only.

January 13th

A personal training session is not the time to eat a meal, snack on a protein bar, or enjoy your caffeine fix. Be sure to schedule breaks in your day to account for your personal needs. It may seem silly, but standing next to your client with a coffee in hand doesn't present an image of a professional who is ready to pay attention. Keep water and nothing more.

When getting into the nitty-gritty of professionalism, it's important to look at all behaviors, no matter how insignificant they may seem. It can feel trivial to focus on such small details, but elite pros know they matter.

That protein bar or pre-workout drink may seem like no big deal to you, but they affect the way you're perceived. Your client and those around you might question your priorities when they see you having a bite or drinking your morning coffee while standing over your client.

Demonstrate that you are fully present for all of your clients' sessions by handling your food and hydration needs in private.

January 14th

Keep the focus on your client in conversation. While a personal training relationship is one that benefits from a mutual interest in each other's well-being, keep in mind who is paying whom. Share your life and thoughts when appropriate, but always put the client first.

For conversation to be most effective and enjoyable, both parties must give and take equally. If one party feels as though they are doing all the talking, then they may begin to shut down and hold back. Just the same, someone who is always listening may feel "talked at" and begin to shut down too.

It is OK to have personal conversations with clients and share details of your own life, but it's critical to get back on topic and focus on them, their goals, and their needs as quickly as possible.

Describing your epic touchdown pass in high school football or yesterday's killer leg workout doesn't help your client get better today. Ask questions about them, their body, and the workout. Most of all, focus your energy and words on coaching cues.

People will always remember how much you cared about them and their lives. That's a big one.

January 15th

Don't talk about matters that wouldn't help you pick up your next client or wouldn't make your mother very happy. It doesn't matter how well you know a client; it's important to keep conversation professional. This means keeping discussions of weekend shenanigans, politics, and religion off the gym floor. Focus on the moment and light-hearted conversation.

Avoiding touchy topics such as religion, politics, and ethics is imperative to keeping your clients engaged in your programs.

Your clients may be the ones initiating the conversation, even begging for your input, but it's important to keep your focus on doing your job while on the gym floor.

The risk of losing a client is too great when such sensitive issues come up during a training session. Similarly, avoid discussing your weekend transgressions and over-indulgences with clients too.

Your reputation requires your commitment to keeping conversation clean and professional. One wrong word can cause damage you can't fix.

January 16th

*The best coaches stand at a respectable distance from
their clients, observing their every move and providing
cues that guide the client to an even better performance. This
can't happen if you are exercising with your client. There is
no professional justification for working out while
your client is paying for your time.*

You cannot justify charging a client to work out with them. It's impossible to provide your client with optimal coaching if you are also exercising.

They are paying you for your expertise, your eyes, and your coaching cues, which you cannot provide if you are focusing on your own body. The exercises you select or the repetition scheme you choose are not what make you a good trainer. To the contrary, it is your ability to coach anything to anyone in a language that they understand.

There is no argument here. If you are receiving money, then your job is to observe, coach, and react. You cannot charge someone to "tag along" and call yourself a trainer, or at least you shouldn't.

January 17th

A great business is prepared a month in advance. Schedule your clients for an entire month at a time to help account for travel, business, and life-happenings. Maintain a steady income, and help keep your clients accountable to their goals, by scheduling their sessions a month in advance.

Living life as it comes at you can certainly be a more fun and loose way of doing things, but it hurts your ability to run a business. You are a single coach who must manage the schedules of five, ten, fifteen, twenty, and possibly thirty people.

Chances are they want the same times on the same days and you'll have to make all the puzzle pieces fit to run your business smoothly and professionally.

On the fifteenth of every month, begin sending out emails to gain client commitment to the following month. Most of the time they'll keep the ball rolling, but other times you'll learn of their travel plans, their need to put a halt on training, or their need to switch time slots. Being prepared for these conversations is critical to your long-term success.

January 18ᵗʰ

*Send emails to your clients at the end of each training cycle
that recap their progress. Each training cycle should have
specific goals laid out at the outset that can be reviewed at
the end. Doing so in person, as well as in written format,
will provide that next level of service that helps set you and
your business apart from your peers by showing you care.*

Feedback is critical for your development as a personal trainer. The insight into what you are doing well and what you are missing the mark on is imperative to developing a great training business.

Choosing to ask for feedback after every training cycle (four to eight weeks) is a great way to keep that conversation open and allow for your client to voice their thoughts about you, your programming, and their progress.

People value being heard and want to know that their opinion doesn't get disregarded in favor of your expertise. Some will say too much, and others will say nothing at all, but the fact that you ask and take things into consideration is what really matters.

January 19th

A great business person understands that customer contact is of primary importance. Pride yourself on answering communication from your clients, prospects, fellow coaches, management, and any other individual within twenty-four hours. In today's age there are few excuses for why you can't respond.

Responding to someone's communication has never been easier, but for some reason, too many personal trainers take their sweet time to answer business-related email.

Answering someone within twenty-four hours demonstrates that you care about their contact and you value them as a person.

Any longer than this window and you run the risk of disrespecting the other person's time and making them disinterested in continuing their working relationship with you.

This doesn't mean you have to be available at all hours either. Establish your "off" hours early in your business relationships to protect your personal space and stay sane.

January 20th

Locate additional equipment prior to a session (mini-bands, agility ladders, etc.) so that your client isn't waiting while you search the facility high and low. Simple things such as this show how much you value a client's time and want to maximize it.

A client is literally paying for time when they purchase training sessions. Yes, your expertise and charisma factor in, but a thirty or sixty-minute session can go by in a flash if you aren't managing time appropriately.

Maximize the time your clients are spending training and cut down on the standing around by locating those little pieces of equipment that always seem to get lost in your facility before you begin.

Consider keeping a bag of mini-bands, sliders, lacrosse balls, pull-up bands, wrist wraps, and whatever else you use with you during a session.

Being prepared goes a long way in proving your professionalism and enhancing your client's experience (and makes it easier to justify paying your price the next time they must renew their sessions).

January 21st

Never gossip to anyone, ever. If you'd like the support of the people around you, then stay above the petty gossip and focus on bringing out the best in all people.

High school behaviors are meant to stay in high school, where teenagers get together and attempt to become adults. A real professional is never whispering in the corner about another coach, another client, or even listening as someone else spews the latest gossip.

Picture yourself as the person being talked about next time you feel the urge to engage in this behavior and consider how it makes you feel. Do you want people talking about your broken heart, personal ordeal, or personality behind your back?

The professional who gets the furthest is the one who treats everyone with respect and honors the communications that they engage in. Your reputation should be one of authenticity and character and not of phoniness and gossip.

Be the person that people want to talk to.

January 22nd

If you are in a position that has a manager, always communicate your needs, successes, and failures on a regular basis. They'll appreciate your clarity and be able to assist you in building and maintaining your business. There is no benefit to holding onto your pride, or fear of rejection, when your business depends on the oversight of someone else.

The saying "the squeaky wheel gets the grease" is a perfect description of how a larger personal training business, such as one at a big-box gym, is managed.

The trainer who communicates with management when they need something, have an opinion, want clarity on a policy, just want to have a friendly conversation, or want to report doing something awesome is the trainer who is often first to come to mind when a new client comes in.

Staying quiet when you are struggling won't build your career any faster. And acting like you're above management when you're doing well is a quick way to make enemies of the people who support you. Be transparent, be fair, and be honorable.

January 23rd

*The best coaches leverage the knowledge, talents,
and energy of those around them to help their clients
achieve their goals. Never see another trainer as
competition. Rather, look to them as another resource for
your clients, an extension of yourself, and as someone
who understands you and your challenges. There are
enough clients for everyone.*

It's understandable: you want to be the best coach in your gym, your region, the country, and the world. Asking for help from someone doesn't support that goal, does it?

To the contrary, it is exactly what supports your growth as a trainer. You'll never know everything. There is simply too much information in the world for one person to reign it all in on their own.

Establish relationships built on respect with the coaches around you and actively learn from them whenever possible. Each trainer has their unique perspective on things and the potential to help you better yourself, and your clients, if you took the time to listen.

Remember, it takes a village to raise a child.

January 24th

Wrap up every session in a similar way, with a moment of reflection about the session and a projection of what your client can expect in the future. This conversation also allows for your client's heart rate to return to baseline while in your presence, which is a safe and professional act.

First, let's acknowledge that walking away from a client who still has a high heart rate is an unprofessional act, no matter what reasoning you could conjure up. Even the healthiest trainees could experience low blood sugar and faint. Individuals with any conditions may experience much worse.

A professional trainer ensures that their client, who is their responsibility, is close to baseline before moving on and ending the session. A concluding conversation is the perfect way to do this.

From a business standpoint, recapping the workout, highlighting client wins, and previewing the next session demonstrate that you care about the individual you are with and are excited for your next meeting.

January 25th

Technology can greatly assist in the tracking and sharing of a client's program and all relevant data. It is not uncommon to see trainers utilizing tablets or phones tapped into the cloud to track a client's workout. This is not an excuse, however, to utilize the device for personal uses such as texting, emailing, or browsing social media.

Technology is both a gift and a curse when placed into the hands of mankind. For every beneficial function there is always another that's sinister. You've seen it in the sci-fi movies repeatedly.

While texting your significant other about dinner isn't akin to taking over the world with a death ray, it is an unprofessional behavior during a training session.

Going digital is excellent for your PT business, but remember to keep it professional when you are on the clock. No social media glances and no group chats on your client's time.

And always ask permission (twice) before filming a client during their workout. Ask before you film and before you post the video.

Your technology can do wonders, but it can do damage. Never forget this simple fact.

January 26th

Trainers obviously want to exercise themselves, but it's important to finish your own workouts at least thirty minutes before a training session. A great coach will be cleaned up, fed, and prepared for the session with time to spare. Being a personal trainer often requires a level of professionalism that can be frustrating at times.

It is our love of training ourselves that often starts the cascade into personal training as a career. Our workouts are our sanctuary, our place away from the noise, and a way of reconnecting with our passion in a kinesthetic way.

But it's important to separate our time from our client's time by ensuring we have wrapped up our workouts, fed ourselves, and made ourselves presentable again before going back into work.

It's not a good look to show up a few minutes late to a session red-faced, dripping sweat, and slamming a protein shake. Be professional and cut your own session short if this could be you. Your client wants to see you at your best.

After all, you have a job to do!

January 27th

Don't bring home life to the gym. Instead, focus on your client and their needs. Your lack of sleep, relationship issues, or personal battles can be discussed when the client isn't paying you. This isn't a recommendation to sweep your personal issues under the rug, but it is a reminder to focus your attention on your client while they are paying for your time.

We all have lives, stress, and issues that hurt and haunt us. As personal trainers we must deal with our issues on our own time and not bring them to the gym with us. Our clients depend on our ability to compartmentalize and do our job.

This doesn't mean a client can't become a friend and help you through trying times—just have discussions about your own life when they aren't paying you for the hour.

To be clear, this does not advocate that you should dismiss your own problems and ignore them. To the contrary, don't be afraid to take some time off and handle what must be done. You can only help others if you've been helped yourself.

January 28th

Avoid confrontation with other members over a piece of equipment. Shine brighter by having versatility and being able to adapt on the fly to meet the needs of your client's program. Squabbling over a flat barbell bench is a waste of time and energy that is better spent training.

The busy hours of your gym could become unbearable if your program requires many of the pieces of equipment that are often in use during this time.

Do your best to program movement patterns and have substitute movements in mind for times when you just can't snag a rack or a bench.

Most importantly though, never engage in an argument with another member or trainer about a piece of equipment while in session. Do your best to work together or modify away from the equipment to present yourself as professional and calm.

The best fitness professionals can seamlessly adapt to a tough situation and still deliver outstanding results.

January 29ᵗʰ

When handling payments, never disappear with a client's credit card. Handle payments through a reputable vendor (Paypal, Square, Swipe) or via your gym's internal system while your client is present. Avoid situations that could lead to anxiety and distrust on behalf of your client.

In a day and age of identity theft and fraudulent charges, you'll want to avoid ever stepping away from your client while handling their credit cards.

Picture your client, nervous about their purchase of sessions and still uncertain as to what type of person you are, anxiously waiting for you to come back from some office with a receipt in hand.

Allow your client to avoid this moment altogether by handling your transactions in clear view. Minimize the time you have your hand on their card and always provide a receipt for your sessions.

You must run your business like a business if you are to be treated like a real professional. Always handle transactions with care.

January 30th

Provide every client with work to do on their own, habits to become better with, and options for classes when they are not with you. Be their go-to person for all that is fitness.

The greatest fitness professionals create a network and in-depth plan for their client instead of creating dependency on themselves.

Supporting your training sessions with great classes, massage therapists, and a network of other fitness-minded people ensures your client is fully supported in their exercise endeavors.

Extending into specific actions or habits that you want them to emphasize each day helps your client build autonomy, which is the goal of any training program.

Instead of worrying about being their only option for fitness content, spend your energy on being the best option that they will always choose.

Never fear losing a client because you've introduced them to a world much bigger than you.

January 31st

Cultivate a relationship with those who don't choose to train with you. Even if someone doesn't have the desire or income to afford your services, your relationship with them may push someone who does your way. Don't spoil your business by only interacting with those who have chosen to pay you.

Your reputation depends on more than just what paying clients say about you. It also relies on the things people who don't train with you say.

Never treat anyone differently because they decided not to train with you or because they train with someone else. You never know who might recommend you. If you maintain the utmost professionalism and treat everyone with the same respect, then you are bound to have fans you barely know.

There is no cost to you to smile, say hello, and ask how someone is doing. There may not be a profit either, but that shouldn't be why you said hello in the first place. Treat every interaction as though they have equal importance.

Be a great *person* and being a great *trainer* becomes much easier.

February

Education

"January is always a good month for behavioral economics: Few things illustrate self-control as vividly as New Year's resolutions. February is even better, though, because it lets us study why so many of those resolutions are broken."

—Sendhil Mullainathan

"An investment in knowledge pays the best interest."

—Benjamin Franklin

February 1st

Your education is only beginning when you complete your degree or earn your first certification. Everything around you can provide a tremendous amount of information that can make you better at your job. Keep your eyes and ears open for learning opportunities.

It is not uncommon to meet a new trainer who thinks they're a superhero once they've finished their certification exam. They've passed a test that does indeed qualify them to be a personal trainer, so they might think they know it all.

However, the best trainers in the world are always learning, always asking questions, and always looking for opportunities to challenge what they believe.

The people around you, the coaches you follow, other certifications, and practical training experience all serve to continue your education and develop you into an outstanding fitness professional.

Seek to learn from everyone and everything and you'll be on your way to your goals.

February 2nd

The letters and certifications you accrue behind your name matter, but they aren't everything. Some of the best knowledge is learned through conversation with other professionals, conference lectures, daily reading, and your own experience.

Our certifications are a defining characteristic in a field where the rate we charge is often tied to what we are qualified to do. In fact, our certifications even serve as a way of comparing ourselves against the rest of the field.

They matter. No doubt about it.

But it is important to remember that they are not substitutions for the lessons taught by the trainers you meet, the teachings of a great blog, or the knowledge gained through an incredible session. They are meant to work in unison and not in opposition.

So, no matter how many letters follow your name, or how few you can lay claim to, realize that you are never done learning. There is always more out there for you to gain.

February 3rd

*Challenge one of your beliefs a day, a week, or a month.
Develop confidence in your beliefs, systems, and messages
by researching with the intent to prove them wrong. This
use of the scientific method allows you to coach clients
without bias since you've done the work to prove your
theory wrong and came up empty.*

It was once said by Thomas Dewar that if you think you know it all, you are missing something. He was wiser than many fitness professionals for sure.

In an industry where certainty makes money you may feel the temptation to "know everything." You'll study up to the point where you have enough science to be right but quit researching before you could possibly be wrong.

It's crucial that you stop believing you are always right and begin challenging your beliefs and practices. You may find that you were off-base and want to change your practices, or you may find that you weren't far off from what is closest to true. Regardless, you are better for verifying.

The mark of an intelligent person is that of someone who has more questions than answers.

February 4th

Being formally educated doesn't always make you a great trainer. A wealth of book knowledge, a research background, and an outstanding IQ can only help you help others so much. One must still communicate, patiently and effectively, what needs to occur during the practical application of this science: a training session.

If a personal training client wanted to hire a textbook, they'd go to a library or a university. Instead, they chose the gym and they chose you.

What does that mean?

It means that all the book knowledge in the world doesn't ensure that you can train a great session. Some brilliant individuals have struggled as coaches because they are incapable of utilizing their knowledge in a real-world setting.

A mastery of the sciences that drive training will propel your career to a new level, but a lack of coaching prowess can slow down your client's progress, or worse, prevent it from happening.

Learn what is necessary for you to think at the highest levels, but constantly seek ways of disseminating the information to those without the degrees or interest in the subject matter.

February 5th

Some certifications do stand out above others. When entering the field or looking to expand your horizons, research how the careers of people who've obtained a certification turned out. The most rewarding educations often have less people earning their designations.

Let's face it, personal training is a lucrative business. Not just for trainers themselves, but for the companies that put out certifications and continuing education. Like any business, not all companies are doing the best work. Many certifications lack the critical scientific, business, and communication materials that could help their students flourish in their careers.

Therefore, it is important for you to do research on the various certifications and who holds them. Are they making good money while enjoying their careers and helping clients get to their goals?

If that answer is no, then maybe you'll want to invest in a more challenging, but more rewarding, certification that opens different doors and qualifies you for increased demands. Your education should equip you for anything.

February 6th

*Read the thoughts of other coaches every day. The age
of the internet has made it much easier to see what
other trainers are doing and thinking because of their
blogs and contributions to website articles. Routinely
browse their content.*

Not all education comes from formal sources. In fact,
some of the best information will come from the blogs
and articles that are written by the top coaches in the
space.

In these free blocks of information, you'll read what
has been on their mind, what they are currently doing
with their clients, and how they solve some of training's
biggest problems. If written well, it feels like you're
enjoying a coffee with these individuals and learning
from them directly.

This form of education cannot replace formal learning
and will often skim over important scientific foundations
that are essential to the success of any training program.
So, be sure to use blogs as a supplement to your standard
learning materials and not as a replacement.

February 7th

Ask your clients for feedback. Sure, they might not be the expert in fitness, but they are the end user and may just have some incredible feedback for you to learn from. Sometimes the student can become the teacher, and in doing so, elevate the teacher to a new level of mastery.

One of the best teachers for a personal trainer will be their clients. Is the program you've been implementing working? Are your clients seeing consistent success in one area or another while still enjoying their experience with you?

Whether or not a client continues showing up and continues to see results is one way of getting a response, but a more specific survey can be used at the end of every training cycle or package to gather even more intel.

Your client may not be the expert in fitness, but they are talented in other aspects of their lives and can provide you tremendous insight into your professionalism, coaching tactics, and overall brand image.

A personal training relationship is one in which feedback can travel in both directions.

February 8th

Discussion is healthy. Have conversations with fellow coaches and debate, respectfully, the merits of a training system, thought process, or method of doing business. The best coaches routinely find themselves in such interactions.

Debate is one of the healthiest forms of information exchange known to humankind. Being pushed to acquire the data necessary to defend or refute a position makes you a better student, and defending your own position helps facilitate a better mastery of what you know and believe.

The key is to ensure that your discussion with other professionals is respectful and built on the intent to better understand topics rather than enforce your own viewpoint.

At the very least, these regular dialogues allow you the opportunity to hear how someone else interprets the same information you've seen, which could help you better coach your clients as you employ new lingo, new cues, and a new viewpoint for the methods you choose.

February 9th

*Education doesn't end between your ears. Your knowledge
is meant to be given as well. Teach those who you can help,
whether they are newer trainers or clients who ask questions
during sessions. One of the best methods of learning a
topic completely is to teach it to someone else. Make this
a common practice.*

The most important thing about education is that it is
meant to be shared. No one has ever benefited from
hoarding information to themselves, or at least not in
the long term.

Remember that no idea you have is uniquely your own. It
is a permutation of something else that someone else has
thought at some other place and time. While it may feel
novel to you, it is merely a variation of what is already
known and accepted.

For this reason, it is crucial that you constantly look
to share what you've learned with anyone interested
in learning from you, especially if they are another
trainer. There may be no greater compliment than to
have another person want to learn from you directly.

February 10th

Being intelligent should never be used as a weapon of judgement. There are many great professionals in a variety of fields who lack extensive formal education but excel regardless. Sometimes the right combination of personality, grit, and humble professionalism can overcome the lack of book smarts in the personal training field. Experience can be a game-changer.

This goes back to the lesson you learned as a kid: don't judge a book by its cover. Back then, it was the clothes they wore to school or whether they had glasses.

Today, as a personal trainer, and especially as one with an outstanding education, never judge a great coach who lacks your pedigree. Your education does not guarantee that you are a better coach or a better professional, and it certainly doesn't make you a better person.

Take the time to learn from the habits and behaviors of those who have made long careers in the industry without the great certifications. Take the time to teach them what you know and improve their game as well. Sharing is caring, after all.

February 11th

*List your education in your written biography, but
never lead with it in conversation. Let someone
experience your personality and skill, instead of flaunting
your accomplishments and pedigree.*

There are few things more annoying than someone shouting off their accomplishments and credentials every chance they get. Clients, prospects, and fellow trainers aren't interested in hearing the laundry list of amazing things you've done.

Sure, it's wise to make sure people can find out about you and your endeavors, but you should never make your resume become your hello. In fact, it should only be a conversation piece when someone asks you about it.

A great habit to get into is listing your credentials and awards in your written biography but omitting them from conversation whenever possible. It's much more impressive when people find out how accomplished you are on their own.

Your conversations should always be centered on how you can help the person you are talking to.

February 12th

Read fiction. It will expand your vocabulary and allow you to escape the analytical brain for a while. Experiencing a well-written story, its landscape, the characters, and the dramatic events as they unfold can reignite the imaginative regions of your brain that help you solve real-world issues.

It can be tempting to take all your reading time and spend it on topics such as science, marketing, and financial wellness. Each of these will improve you as a trainer and a thinker in their own way.

Fiction, however, provides your brain a reprieve from the mundane and the researched and instead fills it with creativity and fantasy. It's the downtown cafés of Hemmingway, the fantastical characters of Charles Dickens, or even the scary settings of Stephen King that set our mind on a path of wonder.

Our conscious brains are overworked in a society that prides itself on data and information gathering, so give it a break by allowing your creative brain to take the reins. You might just find the answer to your biggest problem midway through a novel.

February 13th

*Read non-fiction that is not related to your field.
Broadening your scope to include topics not exclusive
to your field can help make you a more relatable person
capable of holding conversations on a variety of levels.
Moreover, learning how other individuals solved complex
problems may just provide you the solution to your own.
Always work to expand your bubble.*

The field of personal training has so much text and information available that it could feel like it should be all that you read. This book is an example.

Just like you should spend time reading fiction to expand your creativity, spend time enjoying other genres such as business, psychology, finance, biographies, and public health.

The ability to expand your brand beyond training will help you better relate to clients, find inspiring stories about other people, understand business in other industries, and broaden your appreciation for how lucky you are to be doing what you are doing. Priceless.

February 14th

Pay attention to current events. While religion and politics have no place in business, current events show you're plugged in. Don't be the cave man with no idea of how the world around them is being run. Read the top headlines of the day prior to going to work or every night as you wind down. The key is to present yourself as a person with a well-rounded education.

The world is big place with innumerable news events each day. With a twenty-four-hour news cycle available to you through even your smallest electronic device, there's no reason you shouldn't have an idea of what's going on in the world around you.

You don't need to be an expert on politics or a pseudo-reporter or informing your clients of the latest news. Simply stay aware of the world around you and how it could impact you or your clients.

This tip is especially critical if you are employed in a major city around the world, such as Washington, D.C., London, or Shanghai—places where news holds additional weight.

February 15th

The topic of financial health must be explored by every fitness professional. Variable paychecks, uncertain schedules, and the potential to have or not have benefits depending on your employment status can make managing your money hard. Maximize your earnings and secure your future by studying 401Ks, IRAs, the stock market, savings accounts, debt management, tax write-offs, healthy budgeting, and other topics.

Working by the hour, even if you charge a higher rate, isn't the best way to accumulate wealth. Utilizing your income to pay off debts, build savings accounts, and make intelligent investments is.

You are doing a disservice to yourself if you remain clueless about the value of a company-sponsored 401k, the benefits of a private Roth IRA, and how to write off your work expenses during tax season.

Personal trainers must take special care to factor in the vacation months of July and December when business is slower. Investing your money wisely can't happen if you don't spend some personal time learning how the market works.

February 16th

Keep a notebook with you wherever you go. You'll hear things, see things, read things, and say things that you'll want to remember. The best talents in the world are always keeping a running tab of their thoughts, visions, and interpretations. Never forget a great idea again by keeping a notebook on you.

Having a great idea is one of the most invigorating feelings in human existence. Suddenly, a mundane day can be made bright by a eureka moment and the excitement that follows as you chart your path to success.

Forgetting what your idea was is one of the most frustrating feelings. Yet, far too many people experience the excitement of innovation and the disappointment of forgetting in the same day.

Avoid this by keeping a blank notebook with you no matter where you go. You cannot predict when inspiration will hit, when a solution to a problem will appear, or when you'll just want to jot down a few thoughts to review later.

Never be caught empty-handed in a world that only seems to be spinning faster.

February 17th

Coaches, and all people for that matter, should attempt to understand anxiety and depression. You may or may not deal with it yourself at some point, but you'll absolutely encounter someone who struggles daily. Understanding their battle will help you be more empathetic and provide better care.

Almost every living person has experienced anxiety or depression at some point. For most, it's a temporary state attached to an event in their lives.

For others though, it's a constant fight inside of their heads that makes every decision that much harder

to make. For this reason, it's crucial that fitness professionals spend some time familiarizing themselves with the signs, symptoms, and therapies for anxiety and depression.

You may not be qualified to treat them but being empathetic to someone who is struggling internally is one of the best and most human things you could do.

People will always remember that you were there for them when no one else was. Be the person that is there for the ups and the downs.

February 18th

Surround yourself with a community of people
who are smarter than you are. Regular interactions
with people of different careers, but similar drives, will
help you become a well-rounded person. Realize too that
you may be helping them with your words more than
you know. Intelligence moves in circles.

The classic line about being the "average of the five people you spend the most time around" is accurate.

You'll notice that wealthy people tend to hang out with people who are even wealthier than they are, smart people with those who are more so, and fit people with those who they must chase.

They do this because they are driven to become even more and these individuals represent what more "is."

Constantly seek opportunities to be the least intelligent person in the room by joining professional groups, attending seminars, and quietly observing those who have ascended to where you'd like to go.

It is the act of becoming the student again that often helps leaders further their influence and capability.

February 19th

Ask questions of your clients that teach you about who they are as people. Understanding the person in front of you will help you be a better coach, and more importantly, be a better human who provides love and respect. Dive into the story that led them to you and invest yourself in their personal journey through this thing called life. It can be exhausting and personal, but it just may be the calling card of a business that never falters.

Take the time to learn the "why" behind your clients and you'll be better equipped to help them handle their "what" and "how."

We all have stories that are full of twists and turns, highs and lows, and unanswered questions. Choosing to listen to your clients' stories will provide insights about them and lessons about life just the same. It's why we have two ears and one mouth.

Your client who is a successful businesswoman might provide a vision of how she overcame obstacles to get to where she is in life. A few hours later, you might learn that a broken home is why another client developed emotional eating habits.

February 20th

Learn about yourself. Don't be afraid of self-exploration: you'll uncover wounds and understand your strengths. Self-actualization is the greatest gift one can experience. Moreover, you'll provide a more authentic service because of your stable personality. Take the time to reflect on success and failure, missed opportunity and overeager drive, and grow.

Speaking of stories, invest in yourself by listening to your own story. Take the time to write your biography up to this point and then reread it as if the story weren't your own.

Rediscover the wounds you covered up a long time ago, experience the feelings of joy and success that once felt so strong, and remember the ups and downs of the journey that got you right here, right now.

You can better help others when you discover authenticity and comfort within yourself. Your confidence will bleed from everything you do, and your ego will vanish from sight. Self-actualization is one the best forms of education a person could experience, so prioritize your own history from time to time.

February 21ˢᵗ

Study a person you'd love to emulate and another you'd try your hardest to be different from. Look at the traits of the figure you despise and be observant of any similar behaviors that may arise in you when you're emotional or deprived and remove them. Take note of the actions of the person you revere and look to implement them into your daily practice.

Modeling is one of the best forms of self-development when we consider that imitation is a proven form of skill acquisition. The key with modeling lies within the realization that someone can grow both by modeling their behaviors after someone they look up to and modeling against someone they do not hold in high esteem.

Modeling and anti-modeling provide an opportunity to "give one and take one" to yourself and your future.

Emphasizing what you'd like to do more of as well as what you'd like to do less of will ensure that you are always developing your strengths and addressing your weaknesses. Apply this lesson as a trainer and as a person.

February 22nd

Study physics. While you may not need to know how to get a rocket to the moon, it wouldn't hurt to have another context to explain friction, acceleration, and other forces that will appear in the gym setting.

If there is one core science subject that should be understood by personal trainers, it's physics.

The act of exercising subjects the body to forces, both internal and external, over time. Understanding how these forces act on the body and how the body must adapt to handle these forces will improve your ability to coach your clients.

The concepts of gravity, torque, axis of rotation, lever arms, positive and negative acceleration, inertia, and ground reaction force are just a few examples that should be understood by trainers everywhere to safely maximize the training effect on clients.

These key drivers in the world around us are variables that must be understood if we are going to fully realize our potential as coaches of biomechanics and movement.

February 23rd

Set the goal to learn something, however trivial, every day.
It could be how to tie a shoelace that never unties or how
to play the guitar solo in "Welcome to the Jungle." What
you learn matters less than the act of acquiring skills and
expanding your thoughts daily. Besides, weird facts and
talents help set you apart from the ever-growing crowd.

Learning should never stop during your life. Not a single day should go by without you picking up another piece of knowledge, a skill, or refining a talent.

Realize that these things don't always have to align with your career as a trainer either. In fact, it is better for you in the long haul to diversify your learning throughout a variety of subjects and skills.

Read articles on topics that you have no experience in, try to play a musical instrument, learn a new language, or use google to find random facts. What you do daily defines you as a person.

Be defined as a student of everything and be known as the unique individual among the crowd of sameness.

February 24th

An elite mind is capable of not sharing their opinion on a matter until appropriate. You'll look your best when you can bite your lip and let others shine—until your expertise is truly needed in a situation Strive to be the last word, filled with thoughtfulness in its response, rather than being the first and most easily dismissed word.

Investing your time cultivating your expertise can easily influence your drive to share your thoughts with all who have ears. The more you know, the more you'll want to become the teacher.

Caution yourself against the urge to always be the voice in the room. The greatest minds in history have known the value of holding their breath and allowing others to speak before providing their own input.

Silence can be one of the greatest tools of strength in a world where everyone is in a rush to share their opinion on a matter. Wait until you are needed and be remembered for settling an issue once and for all.

February 25th

Education isn't just in books, videos, and memoirs. Travel, eat, drink, listen, and experience the world. As your body and mind experience new things, you'll naturally challenge the comfort zones within yourself. Breaking down these walls can open your mind to possibility and creativity that doesn't come from the daily grind. Knowledge is experienced.

Written word and formalized courses are wonderful means for acquiring and mastering information. However, the greatest teacher is experience itself.

Travel the world, experience new foods, have conversations with people who have radically different backgrounds from you, and say yes to opportunities that you usually say no to.

It is the breadth of your experiences as well as the depth that make you an incredible person. While it's tempting to narrowly focus your efforts on things related only to training, this isn't the best course of action.

Instead, look to leave your comfort zone as often as possible and see the world through new eyes.

February 26th

Don't let becoming an expert in fitness limit you to just fitness. Becoming an expert in multiple disciplines can help you coach people to be better versions of themselves in the gym, out of the gym, and anywhere else they go. Dive into psychology, sociology, and more refined practices of holistic wellness and expand your reach by having more to offer.

Targeting only fitness education will leave you short of your goals.

You are training human beings after all, which involves studying psychology, sociology, epidemiology, and even theology. Remember that you are a human living in a world of humans with a variety of pasts, presents, and futures. Successes and failures stack up in all our lives.

Pride yourself not on being an expert in the field of training, but an expert in the field of persons. Always remember that people will have more life than they have workouts. Become a memorable trainer because you understand humanity.

It is the classic adage:

"People don't care how much you know until they know how much you care."

February 27ᵗʰ

Never stop learning from your parents, caretakers, and elders. Wisdom is real, and heeding the advice of those who've earned their age is never a bad move. Success, failure, regret, and cheer can all arise in the stories of someone who has been around longer than you. Even if the lesson seems like it doesn't make sense at the time, it will eventually.

Age does not automatically imply intelligence, but it absolutely signifies experience. No matter how much you learn in a book, it will never come close to the lessons that can be passed down by someone who has seen more of life than you.

It isn't a matter of merely listening either. Imagine yourself within their stories. How would you act if you wore their shoes?

Listen to them closely enough and you'll realize that you are living a life like theirs, that history does in fact repeat itself, and that you can become better by doing things in a way that honors that fact. You are never too big for sitting down and listening to someone share their life, and experiences, with you.

February 28th

Write constantly. Even if you never publish a word, the act of writing will help you better formulate your opinions and cultivate your ability to string together coherent thoughts. Far too many coaches have intelligent minds and an inability to share quality thoughts with others. Set yourself apart by writing something down every day.

One of the coolest perks of writing frequently is the gift of learning. The act of putting together your thoughts in a coherent manner goes a long way toward developing your beliefs, presentation style, and word usage.

Even if you never publish a word, take the time to write a few hundred words (minimum) each day. Recap your day before you go to bed, describe your feelings on a subject, or write your own version of a news story. What you write about matters much less than that you are writing.

Language has persisted throughout history for a reason, after all. Mastering your use of it will improve your career in ways that won't be clear until you've formed the habit of writing each day. So, go write.

February 29th (LEAP DAY)

Google is all-knowing. Don't come to accept other people's stories, facts, and bluffs. You don't need to call them out, but be comfortable finding the truth for yourself to avoid being led astray. People get second opinions all the time and so should you.

Whether or not you choose to read this tip every four years, this final point is the simplest in this entire book.

In the modern world, we are gifted with the ability to access any piece of knowledge within seconds. No longer do we have to journey hundreds of miles to the capital of our nation and study the scrolls that lie within.

Let's say you are out having lunch with some co-workers and they begin talking about the science that drives our field. Double-check their claims if you don't feel like they are right or look for further information when you get home if they were.

You have the entire world in your pocket when you have Google on your phone. Don't hesitate to go further in your research efforts, and always double-check to verify accuracy.

March

Goal Setting

"Only those with tenacity can march forward in March."

—*Ernest Agyemang Yeboah*

"Setting goals is the first step in turning the invisible into the visible."

—*Tony Robbins*

March 1st

Every person has goals of some sort. Some are less specific than others, but they are unique to the individual nonetheless. It's important to ask questions, dig into the character of your client, and discover their personal goals. Many people may lack the ability to articulate what they want or why they want it, but that doesn't mean they lack desire.

People's goals are as unique to them as other characteristics of their self. When it comes to fitness, however, people often don't know how to describe what they want.

You'll hear a lot of "I just want to get into shape" or "I want to lose weight" as a personal trainer. You could easily take this at face value and start designing your best fat loss and muscle-building program. However, the best coaches in the industry continue to ask questions until specific answers arise.

Why does your client want to achieve their goal? Why did their goal become a goal in the first place? How do they plan to achieve their goals on their own? What do they feel you can add? Ask the right questions before you give guidance, and you'll succeed in nearly every training endeavor.

March 2nd

Follow the SMART method (Specific, Measurable, Attainable, Relevant, and Time-Based) when helping clients set health and wellness goals. Each of these attributes is a critical element of goal setting, and combined, they provide a script for implementing and ultimately achieving goals.

Setting goals requires a plan. Unfortunately, most people skip the planning phase and find themselves with a list of unachieved goals.

Utilizing the well-documented SMART method helps you and your clients get the results you seek. You begin by picking the specific thing you want and add a unit of measure, such as "lose ten pounds" or "earn 5K per month." From there, you must assess the current strategies you employ, all possible changes in strategy, and your available time frame.

This allows you to refine your goals to something like "lose ten pounds in 60 days by exercising daily and eating more vegetables."

A goal must have a plan of attack attached. Otherwise, it's just a dream.

March 3rd

"Out of sight and out of mind" is a common adage that can help declutter an apartment. How many times have you dug through a closet and found something you completely forgot you had? We want to avoid this with clients by prescribing them to place their goals in a visible place that catches their eyes every day. Help them keep their goals "in sight."

How many times have you told yourself that you needed to do something, or had a great idea, ultimately forgetting to follow through?

Your brain has a lot of responsibilities, managing bodily functions and imminent needs, thus making it tough to manage long-term goals and dreams without outside assistance. That assistance comes in the form of your goal being visible to you daily.

Place a note somewhere you'll see, or coach your clients to do so, to ensure that a goal is never forgotten or overtaken by the day-to-day. This very book was built on a series of post-it notes and daily planners to keep things on track.

March 4th

Every new month or training cycle provides an opportunity to have a short discussion with your clients about their goals. How are they doing on goals they've set previously? Have any new goals come to the surface that should take priority? Listen for cues as to where you should take their program next.

A client's goals require constant checking in when working in the field of health and wellness. Between their own thoughts and the ideas planted there by friends, family, and the media, it is often tough for a client to stick to a specific goal.

As a coach, schedule regular check-ins that last no more than five to ten minutes with the intent of confirming, or reconfiguring, a client's goals. Doing so ensures that you are always pushing your clients in a direction that satisfies them while honoring the integrity of your program and the scientific principles that govern our practice.

Obviously, don't let your client change their goals dramatically every training cycle, but always allow for input and course correction.

March 5th

*Every personal training client sets outcome goals, such
as losing twenty pounds, when they talk to a trainer.
However, it's better to develop process goals, such as
exercising five days a week. Weight loss depends on many
factors, but showing up to the gym is completely in the
client's control and will lead to more success.*

The efficacy of goal setting has been proven more
scientifically than most could imagine. Recent years
have brought about scientific findings that goals founded
upon actions, such as going to the gym every day, are
significantly more successful those focused on outcomes,
such as losing ten pounds.

It all comes down to control. Weight loss is so multifacto-
rial that it is quite possible to do everything right and still
and not lose the ten pounds. However, going to the gym
is a habit that can be completely controlled and tracked
all the way until the end of a training cycle. Control what
you can.

Allow your clients to succeed with their goals by
crafting outcome goals: the behaviors for which they
have absolute control.

March 6th

*The power of community is undeniable, so introduce
your client to the idea of sharing their goals with two to
three people in their lives and ask for help in keeping
them accountable. Developing a support community for
a client is crucial to long-term success and may extend
the benefits of healthy living to even more people.*

The power of community can never be overstated.
Having a support system is one of the greatest predictors
of success in any endeavor, but especially in a tiresome
pursuit such as health and fitness.

Help your clients achieve their goals by surrounding
them with people who are on the same path. They may
not be at the same junction, but they do share a similar
road. Picture the bond they'll form when they realize
that they are not alone, and even more, that what they
are trying to do has been done by others.

All clients, no matter how challenging their journey,
will appreciate being introduced and indoctrinated into
a community of people just like them. Everyone likes to
feel like they are a part of something.

March 7th

When faced with day-to-day noise, it's easy to choose the here and now over the long-term goal. Have a client write down every time they do "slip up" and look to identify patterns. Often, it's a lack of preparation that leads to mistakes, such as not having dinner available at home and choosing to stop for fast food on the way. Mistakes provide information for improvement.

Mistakes happen in life no matter who we are. What sets success stories apart from others is a person's ability to learn from undesirable results and improve themselves or their actions going forward.

What will set your business apart is your ability to allow clients to fail and learn—an integral piece of life. If your client goes off the rails for a weekend, then it's most

important that they figure out *why* they did so instead of focusing on *what* they did.

If your clients, and you, can track your mistakes over time, you'll better understand the trends and situations that cause the stumble in the first place. This is the information that leads to change.

March 8th

Focus on goals that center around adding something beneficial to a client's life over those that remove something pleasurable (even if it's bad for them). Adding in multiple servings of vegetables, additional glasses of water, and an extra hour of sleep can help someone lose weight faster than telling them to never eat chocolate, drink alcohol, or skip the gym.

It's easy to tell someone to stop a behavior that we know, and they probably know, is bad for them. When a client asks us about how they can lose some weight, it's easy to say things like:

"Don't eat sweets or drink sodas."

"Don't stay up late."

The advice isn't bad, of course. It can help someone lose weight if they listen to you. However, this "take" causes a level of protest from your client (even if it is silent). They'll nod their head and agree, but deep down resent you for being so strict.

Instead, focus on adding behaviors that promote healthy living prior to taking anything away. Coaching someone to eat more vegetables is a much safer place to begin your coaching. Think about "giving" behaviors.

March 9th

There will be setbacks on the road to achieving any goal. It's critical to realize that the path to success is more of a zig-zag and less of a straight line. Your clients, no matter how logical they promise to be, will forget this when they get stressed about progress. Remind them that the journey to anywhere meaningful never takes a direct path.

No one bats 1.000 in life. In baseball, you can even be considered a Hall of Famer if you only get on base three out of every ten at-bats. Give your clients this same room to operate and you'll find they succeed in the long term.

It's more effective to allow clients to work with you without fear of letting you down. You are their coach and not their parent, preacher, or deity. Judgement must be left out of all conversations with a client.

Investing the time to coach your clients about the frustrating randomness of weight loss, the grind that is muscle gain, and the normality of feeling like quitting is important to their progress and the reputation of your business.

It's why they put erasers on pencils.

March 10th

Preach the benefit of doing small tasks every morning to your clients. Something as simple as making the bed, cooking in advance, or handling lingering tasks can set the course for a successful and productive day. Checking off to-do list items can be addicting and drive someone to go to the gym even when they don't "feel like it."

Achieving your goals can be intimidating at times, no matter how driven you are. It can feel as though you are at the base of a large mountain with so much work and uncertainty ahead. It can paralyze you with its magnitude.

Which is why it's essential to start every day by accomplishing a few small, trivial goals that require minimum effort and time. Things such as making your bed, hard-boiling a few eggs, and reading ten pages of a book could be enough to swing the energy of the day toward achievement.

Momentum is a key asset when we look to elevate ourselves toward our goals. Coach yourself and your clients to begin every day with small wins and soon enough you'll find the drive to take on bigger, and more challenging, tasks.

March 11th

*Establish a "why" behind bigger goals. Providing context
as to why a goal may change your life or make you happier
is important to staying on the path to accomplishing it.
Inform your clients about the "why" behind many of
your training and nutrition recommendations.*

We must peel back the layers of our own onion and understand our motivations that lie below the surface. This applies to your clients too.

The goals we achieve are usually the ones that are centered behind a deeper "why": the ones that fill our minds as we fall asleep at night, the ones that cause us to feel something in our body when we talk about them.

Take the time to discover the why that drives you and your client's goals. Separate the meaningful goals from the fleeting ones and pour all your energy and programming into achieving the important ones.

Success is much easier to achieve when we know why we are working so hard. It gives context to our struggle and gives hope to our outcomes. Always know "why."

March 12th

*In fitness, goals should be separated into three categories:
Aesthetics, performance, and wellness. These categories
allow you to help your client see that there is so much
more to exercise than physical appearance. Helping a
client lose weight while learning how to do ten perfect
pushups and ending their knee pain is something that
we should all aim to achieve.*

Help your clients see the benefits of a fitness program
that extends beyond the weight on the scale or the
reflection in the mirror.

Granting clients the gifts of performance and pain-free
living are selling points for future sessions, points of
empowerment for their character, and incredible results
that shouldn't be swept under the table.

Provide your clients with an opportunity to set goals
within the three categories mentioned in the tip above.
You will empower them by granting them multiple
avenues for which they could be successful with you
and your training.

Our role as fitness coaches requires us to guide clients
towards living their best life. Our clients depend on us
to know what that is.

March 13th

Goal accomplishments deserve an award. Encourage them to enjoy a dinner with friends and family after they've achieved a big training goal or completed a physical feat. But, be sure to remind them that they must jump right back on the wagon as soon as possible.

The reward center of our brain doesn't just go away because we are trying to do something good and healthy, such as lose weight.

Therefore, it is important to coach your clients to take a step back and enjoy a treat, or an experience, once they reach their goals. The key is to teach them that this reward must be enjoyed guilt-free.

We must help clients break the attitude of "all-or-nothing" by ensuring they can enjoy their lives when possible.

Still, a guilt-free reward is not a ticket to a step backward in training and lifestyle. Remind your clients that once the reward has ended, they must get back on track and return to their habits of excellence.

A loyal client is one who enjoys their success while looking forward to your next challenge.

March 14th

Allow your clients to explore the "why" behind their actions. Someone who binge eats or sleeps poorly may have problems that go well below the surface we see. Don't be afraid to recommend a psychologist to your clients who struggle with issues that go beyond your scope. Sometimes though, a little advice and a listening ear can be just what they need.

The "why" behind our goals has already been discussed, but what about the "why" behind our actions?

We must explore why we do the things we do each day, especially when those things derail us from our goals.

Looking into a client's behaviors and finding out why they may binge on weekends, can't stay in on a Friday night, or refuse to eat breakfast is critical to finding the right coaching strategy for them.

Sometimes there are deeply woven struggles in the fabric of the person you work with. Other times it's just downright laziness and a lack of preparation. Knowing the difference is *the* difference to having a successful business full of successful clients singing your praises.

March 15th

Research can be a fantastic guide for goal setting. One must understand what is possible and what is not. There will always be a client who thinks they can lose an immense amount of weight in a short period of time even though the science doesn't show this as possible. Be sure to be honest and clear about how the science works.

Often, our clients show up looking to make dramatic changes in less time than is possible. The classic twenty pounds in a month comes to mind.

As professionals, we must keep in mind what is possible with the body, so we don't oversell or underdeliver results with our clients.

At times, you may have to push the research you've done onto your clients' plates and allow them to digest it themselves. Bias, hope, and dogma all fight against your recommendations as a professional trainer, even if you've done your homework.

You may have a few uneasy interactions, but your honesty will be appreciated by your client: the person desperate for change and willing to pay for it.

The right knowledge is always powerful.

March 16th

Help clients set realistic goals at the beginning of their journey with you. Losing a large amount of weight or becoming the next Thor may sound like what they want, but too big of a goal is going to intimidate them at their first sign of struggle. Focus more on process goals that are easy to accomplish and create a winning streak for your clients.

Building off yesterday's lesson is today's point of setting realistic process goals at the beginning of your relationship with your client. There is nothing you can gain by promising the world to your client only to deliver a small globe from an airport shop at the end.

Never fear losing a client because you won't promise to do the impossible. In fact, hold steady in your practice of building safe and sustainable programs for your clients. You may even have to say no to some business along the way.

It's critical for the success of your clients, and ultimately your reputation, that you deliver the results your clients desire, so long as they respect the laws of science.

March 17th

Help your client develop strategies for getting through those sticky points. It's easy to point the finger and tell your client what to do, but a much better approach would be to get in the dirt with them. So, stand by your clients when the going gets tough and provide avenues for them to move onward.

Handing out advice is the easiest thing a fitness professional can do. It doesn't take much skill or effort to sit back on our high horse and say, "do this" or "don't do that."

The best coaches are always willing to get down to their client's level and explore the problems that face them. This is especially true when it comes to conversations regarding nutrition and recovery habits.

Take the time to explore the uniqueness of your client and their situation, and prescribe an equally unique solution. Your patience will be rewarded with a loyal client who stays with you even after they've achieved their initial training goals.

Always meet your clients where they are and slowly walk them to where they should be.

March 18th

*A daily to-do list serves as an excellent reminder of tasks
that need to be completed to reach the goal. Whether it's
for you as the coach or for your clients, it's important to
create a running list of behaviors and actions that must
be completed to move forward.*

Breaking down larger goals into smaller ones that
are easier to manage and achieve is not a new idea.
However, cutting the goal into daily tasks that add up
over time is a step that many clients and coaches miss
the mark on.

Take your client's goal to build five pounds of muscle
and create a smaller goal of five gym appearances each
week and another goal related to calorie consumption.

Breaking these down to daily tasks means that the client
has their workout planned for the day (hopefully training
with you) and their meals cooked and ready to go for easy
consumption.

By breaking down bigger goals into daily tasks, a person
is better able to succeed every day of their program with
you.

March 19th

Habits must exist before goals are accomplished. A habit is something that we are compelled to do without thinking about it. In health and wellness, emphasizing developing better habits as a goal is best for long-term success. Something as simple as starting every day with a glass of water and five minutes of meditation can change someone's entire life.

Motivation is fleeting. It can come and go like the rain. Habits, however, are much more unbreakable.

Coach yourself and your clients to establish habits of excellence: things they do each day that ensure they are moving toward their goals and improving their life.

Things such as moving every day, eating enough vegetables, drinking water when they wake up, calling their parents once a week, writing in a nightly journal, or enrolling in a monthly savings plan are all habits of successful people.

It is important to not force specific habits on your clients though. As they say, different strokes for different folks. Allow your clients to "choose" their own way with your nudging.

things that aren't related can make it hard to achieve success.
Each little goal gets significantly harder when other goals
pull them in a counterproductive direction. You wouldn't
want a client trying to increase their deadlift max while
training for a marathon.*

Setting goals does require a bit of logic. While the saying
"aim for the stars" looks great on a high school classroom
wall, it lacks the specificity needed for success.

More importantly, goals must be like each other when we
want to accomplish multiple things at once. For example,
training for a powerlifting meet while trying to lose weight
is going to make improving one's strength exceptionally
challenging.

Just the same, getting someone to cut back on their
caloric intake while they are training for a marathon
is counterintuitive.

For your typical client, it could be as simple as matching
their lower calorie plan to the lower intensity phase of their
program—a logical pairing that enhances the chance of
success.

Day by Day

March 21st

Choose one major goal at a time. For example, it is common to prescribe increased exercise and decreased caloric intake to someone looking to lose weight. Can you realistically expect this person to work out so frequently when they have no energy?

To piggy-back off yesterday's tip: it's crucial for us coaches to match the intensity of a client's program with the number of calories they are taking in.

You cannot successfully train someone to build muscle, burn body fat, get stronger, and run a marathon at the same time. Even if you did apply stress in all these areas, your results would be limited by the presence of the other goals: there would be too many ropes pulling in too many directions.

Ensure your clients achieve success by emphasizing one major goal, such as weight loss, at a time. Put all effort into that goal for six to eight weeks before rotating toward another goal set, like building muscle.

Brick by brick every great structure is built.

March 22nd

Provide your clients with a place to track their goals.
Whether you design a spreadsheet or utilize an app that
allows you to share information, stay in touch with them
and be their guide as they work toward each accomplishment.
The act of entering data that they know you'll see should
push them to work harder and remain honest.

Don't leave your clients in the wilderness with your plans. Provide them with documents that help them track habits, record workouts, and even log the foods they consume.

There are plenty of services out there, and more coming, that allow you to take care of your clients' needs from one digital place. However, these come with a price tag.

A much more cost-effective but time-consuming method is to create your own documents that have your brand front and center. Whether they are logging their food intake or jotting down the weights they lifted during your off-day program, they'll see your logo and know that you are the person who is changing their lives.

March 23th

Progress requires a frequent push in the right direction, especially when changing tough habits. Look to communicate with your clients at least three times per week when they are not training with you. It doesn't need to be much more than a text, but the goal is to be omnipresent in your client's life.

As mentioned in the previous tip, it's important to stay in contact with your clients as they embark on a challenging journey with you.

While exercise and dieting behaviors might come easily to you and your peers, these very same actions are complete disruptions to your client's everyday way of life.

A thoughtful text before a Friday evening dinner could be enough of a reminder to make the right choices. Go one further by asking them to send you a weekly email that summarizes their life when you weren't around.

Stay engaged with the twenty-three hours of each day that you aren't with your client. It doesn't need be excessive, but your clients need to know you are there.

March 24rd

Goal achievement can be addictive. As your client shows progress and succeeds in one goal, be sure to follow it up with another. Capitalize on the high that comes from becoming a champion in one area by setting the bar in the next. Endorphins are powerful tools of successful businesses and coaches.

How good does it feel when you finally accomplish the thing that has been out in front of you for as long as you can remember?

Some climb literal mountains while most of us keep it metaphorical, but either way, it's important to find your next peak as soon as you can, regardless of what your mountain looks like.

Guide your clients to enjoy their success and experience the euphoria that accompanies it but to also begin setting their next goal into their sights.

Their next goal may not even be training-related, but your job as their coach is to support them and help them realign themselves to achieve the next goal on their list.

Show them a world of possibility.

March 25th

Volunteer to experience a goal with your client. Maybe they want to attend a yoga class every week and don't feel comfortable to do so on their own yet. Attend with them for the first few weeks and show your support while also spending time practicing a discipline that benefits you. Grow with your clients.

There is no better way to demonstrate that you support someone than to actually show up and support them in their efforts.

Say a client is feeling the itch to go for a long run but is hesitant to make such a push on their own. Then lace up your shoes and hit the pavement with them. The same goes for yoga classes, cooking classes, and even volunteer work for the community. Show that you support your client's growth by standing beside them when you can.

If you want to show someone that you care, then show up to something they care about. Remember this and you'll always know the right thing to do when it comes to your clients.

Need a final push? Think about how you felt when someone you cared about was there for you. Pay it forward.

March 26th

Implore your clients to study the paths of people who shared their goals. In the age of the internet, there are thousands of blogs that people have written that document their struggles and intentions. Motivation, problem-solving, and understanding can come from other people's experiences. Harness the power of the collective to help a client along their journey.

The saying goes, "History repeats itself." This is typically stated when studying politics, world conflict, or the trends that pop culture tends to follow.

It also applies to the endeavors we take on as individuals too. Thousands of people have lost weight before, thousands of others have put on muscle mass, learned to run races, or lift barbells. The point is this:

There is someone out there with a journey not unlike your client's.

Help them find inspiration in the stories, for better or for worse, that have preceded their efforts. Maybe they'll find the right nugget that makes success more of a certainty.

March 27ᵗʰ

*Motivation is overrated. Coach your clients to just start
doing things. Writing a book starts with just one word.
Action is always better than contemplation. We often wait
as though there will be a perfect eureka moment in our lives
that will push us toward what we need when in reality,
eureka will never come if we don't move now.*

As stated previously in this chapter, motivation can be fleeting. One day you'll wake up and feel ready to conquer the world while others you'll want to crawl back under the covers and wish for a better tomorrow.

You must take the good with the bad and move toward your goals, which is why action is always best. Even if you only do a few things, do those things, because not doing them only causes you to fall further behind your hopes and dreams.

Coach your clients to make sure that they always take at least one step toward their goal each day. The habit of moving forward will persist even when life pushes us backward a few steps.

Get your clients in motion, any motion, and the rest tends to fall in line.

March 28th

Part of goal setting is planning for failure. It's rare that something goes perfectly according to plan, so it's critical to have fallback goals in place for those times when what's optimal just isn't going to happen. If a client wants to lose ten pounds in two months, then begin expressing their outcome in the form of a range, say seven to ten pounds, each time you talk.

One of the worst ways to approach any goal is to maintain an "all-or-nothing" attitude. You must understand that in any endeavor, something could go wrong, and honestly, it probably will.

This makes it important to coach our clients to build in a little bit of "failure" expectation into their goals by giving themselves a target that looks more like a range and less like a singular digit. For example, losing eight to twelve pounds over the course of two months instead of a strict ten.

Doing so doesn't lessen one's effort or even sell someone short. It helps maintain momentum through the ups and downs of life. Remember, nothing is perfect, so don't expect it.

March 29th

Goals aren't permanent. It isn't uncommon for someone to make it down a road, even halfway, and realize that it isn't what they want. Don't force someone to complete something simply because it was written down. If they speak with conviction, then be willing to shift your program and guide them toward what they truly desire.

Goals are as flexible as they need to be. More importantly, goals aren't written in stone and are subject to change based on the desires of the person setting them.

A client might begin a program focused on building muscle and strength but soon realize they'd rather lose the unnecessary body fat first. Your job as a coach is to honor that ask and rewire your systems to make this possible.

This doesn't mean you bend and adapt to every whim of a client though. You are the paid professional after all. The point here is to never be more rigid than needed when it comes to setting and maintaining course with a client's goals.

Think of how your GPS can find a better route for you when traffic occurs. This is no different.

March 30th

Developing goals isn't easy. It can be hard enough to predict where you'll be in twenty-four hours let alone where your body or mind will be in a year. Focus on the manageable and allow the skill of goal setting to develop within your client. Like anything in life, "practice makes perfect."

Read any business or self-help book and you'll find yourself thinking that goal setting should be easy. You'll close that final page wondering if something is wrong with you because your goals aren't crystal clear visions in your head.

Trust that you are normal and realize that setting goals that are far off in the future is much harder than an entire industry of writers wants to lead you to believe.

If your goal or a client's goal seems small, then make double sure that you crush that goal and move onward to the next. If your goal is too big, then break it down into smaller, manageable actions until you get to your destination.

Unlike movies, life can't be scripted perfectly, no matter how hard we try.

March 31ˢᵗ

Goals keep us honest. Goals keep us focused. Goals can also blind us from the variety of life. Remember that our goals are critical parts of our drive to succeed, but we must honor the subtle deviations in the day-to-day that make us human. Missing a workout to see a friend you haven't seen in ages is far more meaningful than another night of squats. Seriously.

Goals are an important tool for anyone with a desire to be successful in this ever-changing world full of opportunity and failure. They are the bread and butter of our life's meal.

Yet, far too often we go head over heels into chasing our goals and forget to look around at the beautiful world. You probably know someone who worked forty years without blinking but missed his kid's graduations, birthdays, and was divorced before he could even realize it.

Chase your goals, but only to the point where they improve your life. Never let them steal your life.

Don't let the destination deprive you of the journey and the views it provides.

April

Program Design

"Here cometh April again, and as far as I can see the world hath more fools in it than ever."

—Charles Lamb

"Building an exercise program is a lot like bringing a recipe to life. There's a certain amount of ingredients available to us, and a seemingly endless number of ways to put them together."

—Kevin Mullins

April 1st

A program, like the person doing it, is a living organism. A great training program adapts with the ebbs and flows of the client. Always design your programs to have regressions for the less-than-optimal days and progressions for the days when everything is firing correctly. This flexibility will ensure progress is made in some manner each session.

Only a foolish trainer would write a program in concrete. Training a human being, a living organism, requires a certain level of flexibility in exercise design.

Imagine your client coming to you after a week-long business trip that involved twenty-plus hours in the sky crossing the ocean. Picture how tight and sore they feel after being stuck in a metal tube for nearly a day.

The best coaches regress the program and look to conquer the world another day.

Just the same, a highly caffeinated, well-rested client might be ready for a progressed version of their normal program. Be ready to adapt.

April 2nd

Exercise programs are unique to everyone. Of course, there is plenty of science that justifies exercise methodologies, but nothing is one-size-fits-all. It's important to acknowledge the differences between people and account for them in your exercise programs.

People come in a variety of body shapes and sizes. It's important for a personal trainer to acknowledge the opportunities and limitations that someone's limb length, bodyweight, and flexibility present. For example:

- Tall athletes have very different biomechanics than that of a shorter individual. Their squats, hinges, and gait patterns are going to look dramatically different.
- People who carry a lot of weight around their midsection have a harder time in push up and plank positions, as well as getting into a full hinge.

Each client provides a unique canvas on which you can paint a masterpiece. The paint should match the canvas and not the other way around. Be an artist of the highest quality by treating each work as its own masterpiece.

April 3rd

Develop a program that has the end in mind. A great coach understands that achieving a client's goals requires envisioning a path from now until completion. Avoid the temptations of WODs and emphasize developing a unique program that has at least the next six weeks of workouts in mind for your client.

A responsible and successful trainer is someone who develops and executes a plan for their clients. While the rest of the world has gone mad and emphasizes workouts that change each day, you need to hold the line and focus on a program that is unique to your client.

Progress does not arise from singular, powerful shocks given to the body, such as what is found in a "workout of the day." Rather, the progressive overload stimulus, meaning small adaptations over time, is what causes the body to change.

This sort of slow and steady progress is exactly why the tortoise beat the hare.

Develop a roadmap for your clients that includes where they are, where they want to go, and as many stepping stones in between accounted for.

April 4th

The best exercise programs account for what a client is currently capable of performing well and does not overreach. While barbell back squats may be a great exercise to build strength and muscle in the lower body, it may not be appropriate for a client, yet. Instead, tempo goblet squats, single leg squat to stands, and traditional mobility/stability work may be best. Everything is a process in personal training.

Imagine a world where every client does the same exercises as you, as each other, and as dictated by the gold standard that is social media. Wouldn't that just make things easy?

Maybe it would, but the fact is that everyone will have a different entry point when it comes to exercise selection. One client could be perfectly fine deadlifting with a barbell while another must emphasize unloaded hinge patterns. This doesn't mean one person is training harder than the other — it just means they are training appropriately.

Focus on choosing the exercises that your clients can do successfully, time after time, to build your working sets around. This sort of specificity always pays off.

April 5th

Assessments should dictate at least the first six weeks of your program. Without assessments, you are incapable of choosing the correct starting place for each client and may risk injury. Appropriate assessments will examine mobility and stability, the quality of the major movement patterns, and any issues with general fitness.

No one should ever take a client from "hello" to a hard workout before assessing them. A trainer must be able to see what a client can do, what presents challenges, and what absolute limitations may be in play.

An example of a great assessment would be the Functional Movement Screen. This tool provides seven specific tests that can identify issues with client mobility and stability at a variety of joints and with specific patterns.

Acknowledging these strengths and weaknesses is critical to choosing the right exercises, the right loads, and the right correctives as you design your client's program.

Once on that path, the exercises you choose and the workouts you prescribe often serve as enough evidence for any reassessments.

April 6th

Understand that every exercise is nothing more than an application of science. The exercise doesn't make the program—the intention does. The point is to match intentions with desired results. The difference between variations of an exercise depends more on a client's ability level than it does on the excellence of any exercise.

A program must be designed with the intention to cause change. That change is typically measured in pounds lost, pounds moved, or pounds of muscle gained. Yet, it's important to also measure the quality of someone's movements, especially when loaded.

Choose an exercise that fits your client here and now. Overshooting can lead to injuries at worst or a missed opportunity to move the proverbial needle at best. The right load at the right time is exactly what leads to adaptation.

Picture your client struggling with a single leg exercise variation because you are determined to make them do it with two dumbbells instead of another implement. Could they learn the pattern better using another method?

Mastery is a process and not simply a destination.

April 7th

Don't rush to the barbell. A barbell is an advanced implement meant for use by those who are comfortable with it and the loads it can hold. There are no benefits to a barbell exercise that can't be recreated with a dumbbell, kettlebell, or other means if the client isn't ready for loaded barbell lifting.

Once again, we look at the fact that the exercises we select in our programs matter much less than the intention behind each exercise. There is nothing better about a barbell back squat or a barbell deadlift when compared to a goblet squat or trap bar deadlift.

This may sound like blasphemy to many trainers and lovers of the barbell, but follow along: when training someone, it all boils down to what they can successfully complete.

A flawed barbell squat will promote less growth than a perfect goblet squat, even when the load is much less. The key with loaded patterns is to optimally load the individual and not the implement. Keep this at the forefront of your mind when you design your programs.

April 8

Skill acquisition must always precede loading. If a person doesn't understand how to hinge, then how could you comfortably load them with a deadlift? The best coaches spend quality time grooving and improving the movement patterns of their clients prior to loading these patterns. Once a client learns a pattern, it's important to always check back in, every session, with a warm-up drill that helps reset the movement to its optimal form.

Loading an exercise is a privilege and not a right. A client shouldn't be loading any pattern that they aren't comfortable doing without your careful eyes.

The hip hinge is the best example of this: a client who doesn't quite understand how to go through a full hip flexion/extension cycle shouldn't be adding load to the pattern yet.

Using correctives, activations, and other tricks can teach a client how to hinge, which opens the door for loading the pattern in following sessions. Over time, you will be able to train the pattern harder but will always want to check back in with some correctives to ensure the client has retained mastery.

April 9th

Movement patterns are the core of any great program. Every coach should understand that the seven major movement patterns dictate everything else in the gym. An exercise is simply executing one of these movements in a more specific way. A program should have each of the seven patterns in a given training week to ensure a balanced training approach.

Training a human by their musculature is common practice amongst personal trainers. This method isn't wrong, but it isn't optimal for most individuals who purchase personal training.

The reasoning behind this is that all muscles are recruited in some manner when we emphasize movement patterns in our training programs. We are one integrated unit and not just a series of isolated muscles. Our training must reflect this fact by emphasizing patterns.

By training vertical and horizontal push/pull patterns, hinge, knee dominant, gait, and rotation, a client will experience full muscle recruitment in their program.

April 10th

Gait, or locomotion, is the forgotten movement pattern in training books. Your client walks, probably runs, and maybe sprints at some point in their life. They also get up and down from the ground. Shouldn't you make sure they do all these things correctly? Improving gait can make all the difference in a fitness program, especially with someone who is deconditioned or is in the senior population.

Barring any unique or unfortunate circumstances, we can agree that every client must utilize gait in their everyday lives.

Gait is a gross term for our locomotive abilities, otherwise known as walking, jogging, running, and crawling. These patterns are integral to a client's life, yet we often neglect coaching these movements and improving their quality.

Often, it's because we lack the refined eye to adjust what we see, while other times gait is an afterthought. Begin integrating gait training into every client's program and ensure that they can navigate the world, and your workouts, with excellence.

April 11th

Pairing movement patterns together in a superset is a popular strategy that has been employed for years in fitness. However, many of these strategies are often used to further break down muscle tissue and increase intensity of a given workout, which is fine if a client can handle it. For other clients though, consider pairing together a movement pattern that they can train with load with one they are still developing (without load).

What if all your supersets weren't emphasizing intensity or fatigue?

Rather, build a program that stacks a loaded, challenging exercise (such as a deadlift) with an unloaded movement, such as hip bridge, wall angel, or even a snippet of animal flow.

Imagine how much more you'll be able to accomplish if your clients pair challenging exercises with ones that improve mobility, stability, or coordination.

This allows the typical client to recover from the primary exercise while still working toward a positive end goal with your secondary movement. Two birds, one stone.

Imagine the progress your client could make using this methodology.

April 12th

*Don't rush to create physical change in a client. Sure,
they are paying you to provide them results, but they are
also trusting you to keep them safe. If a client presents
movement deficiencies, injuries, or pain, then it's important
to do what is necessary to improve these factors (potentially
referring out to a physical therapist). Don't risk injury
in favor of the sweat economy.*

This is a real catch-22 for personal trainers. Clients sign on with us because they believe we can deliver the results they want: burning fat, building muscle, and contouring the body they desire.

However, we are the professionals in this relationship and must remain calm under that pressure and stay focused on doing what is best for a client in the big picture.

A true professional can create metabolic effect, challenge working muscles, and satisfy a client's wants while still respecting their structural and functional needs.

So, ask yourself: *Am I rushing my client's results and putting them at risk?*

Hopefully not.

April 13th

Ensure that you prepare every client for a training session with an intelligently designed warmup. Designing a mobility flow that addresses a client's specific troubles, activation exercises for the core and glutes, guided self-myofascial release for blood flow, and specific preparations for the day's challenges are a perfect start to any training session.

Picture your client on the treadmill, walking on a slight incline for five to ten minutes, and jumping right into their first working set of an exercise.

If this thought makes you cringe, then good. If not, then take special care when reading this. A client must be properly warmed up prior to engaging in the training program that you've designed for them.

Foam rolling, mobility exercises, core activations, and form-specific movements must take place prior to diving into loaded or ballistic movements.

Always design a warmup protocol unique to the individual and the demands of a given workout. You wouldn't put gas in your lawnmower if you are going to drive your car one-thousand miles.

Be prepared for the journey ahead.

April 14th

Develop a ladder of progressions and regressions of the seven major movement patterns to keep on hand while designing clients' programs. This ladder of seven to ten exercises (of the same pattern) provides you with a thoughtful path for advancing or stepping down an exercise to better suit a client. Not all clients will reach the top rung, nor will every client need the bottom, but it is beneficial to have a measuring stick.

Designing a customized program for someone is not an easy task when you begin factoring in all the data you'll collect during an assessment.

Save yourself time and frustration by sitting down and designing "ladders" of progressions and regressions for each major movement pattern (such as the squat, hinge, or horizontal push).

There should be unloaded and loaded options in your ladder. Your highest rung may be an exercise that only your top 3% of clients would attempt, like a barbell back squat with a pause. Meanwhile, your bottom rung would be accessible to all but offer more moderate results, such as a sit to stand from a bench.

@

April 15th

Build your programs to reflect your client's goals without compromising integrity. Many clients want to lose weight but desperately need to get stronger in places such as their hips, legs, back, and core. While it may seem obvious to put them on a strength program, it may also upset the client when they aren't losing weight after six to eight weeks, even if they've gotten stronger. Instead, incorporating wants and needs into the same program might be your best protocol.

Our jobs as personal trainers is to help our clients achieve what they want while honoring what they need (but don't know they need). Remember that we were hired to perform a task, like any other service industry.

That task is to get the client to their end goal safely. We are often tempted by bias and a desire to fix everything and find ourselves far from where our clients want to go.

Never let your passions or education take you so far away from their wants that you lose the client's trust, or more importantly, that they lose faith in personal training as a means of success.

April 16th

*All clients fit into metaphorical buckets. Some want to
lose weight while others want to get bigger, stronger, or
faster. Separate your clients into categories so that you
can save time when programming. Every bucket might
have five to ten templates saved on your device that can
be adapted to the specific needs of the specific client. This
way you'll maintain the uniqueness of each program
while optimizing your time-at-work.*

There is no need to overwork each time you need to
design a training program. Having eight to ten templates
for each client type can help you save a lot of time when
developing your programs.

Some client types include muscle gain, fat loss, correctives
and post-rehab, strength development, general fitness,
and sports performance. Each of these buckets requires
specialized programs that allow for the client to succeed in
the area they desire.

Once you have these templates designed, you'll be able
to tweak the programs to fit the unique needs and wants
of each new client as they sign on.

April 17th

Training density is a measure of success in a session.
You only have so much time with a client, which forces
you to optimize your programs and make the most of each
minute. Improving density (volume divided by time) is one
method. Volume is load multiplied by sets and repetitions.
D = (Load x Sets x Repetitions) / Time to complete.

A paid training session trades a fixed amount of time for pay. Your time in a session is rather fixed, typically at 30 or 60 minutes. This allows for you to measure density.

Picture this: if it takes me ten minutes to squat 5 sets of 10 reps of 100 pounds, then we can conclude I have a 500 pound per minute density.

This number could be improved week over week by manipulating any of the variables above. For example, lifting more weight in the same time or taking less time to lift the same amount of weight. Both drive density numbers upwards.

Increasing training density increases demands on the metabolism, working musculature, and the cardiovascular system. The result of these things is nothing short of results and a happy, albeit tired, client.

April 18th

While arguably the most popular training method, bodybuilding isn't the best strategy for the average personal training client. The methodology doesn't account for movement quality or the increased need for recovery amongst deconditioned individuals. This doesn't mean you can't steal from bodybuilding programs, but it does mean you shouldn't use one wholesale with a client who isn't ready.

So much of what we do as professionals and as practitioners of exercise comes from the world of bodybuilding. Everything from Arnold Presses to drop sets is a product of a bodybuilder and bodybuilding culture. The list is nearly endless. And it's awesome.

But bodybuilding isn't always the answer to your client's needs. In fact, most of your clientele will need significantly less isolation work and a lot more movement-based training to change their lives.

The isolation and fatigue found in bodybuilding programs has a place in your program, but it shouldn't be the centerpiece for much of your clientele.

April 19th

Powerlifting has a place in everyone's program, but it's important to know the difference between lifting with the intent to maximize your strength and lifting with strength to maximize the effects of a session. Emphasizing only a few movements and high load is not the best approach for most clients you train. Some will crave this approach, but most will not benefit from emphasizing near maximum loads on a consistent basis.

Powerlifting, like bodybuilding, is a tremendous methodology of training that has changed bodies, changed lives, and created some of the strongest humans alive.

However, it is not a one-size-fits-all type of program. The rigors and demands of near-max load lifting are not for everyone, nor will they appeal to everyone. Truthfully, most clients will want to lift "heavy" only as frequently as they must to achieve their goals.

Utilizing phases in your program where a client goes heavier to improve strength is the best practice for most of your business. Those who crave powerlifting will reveal themselves in their training goals and training demands.

April 20th

CrossFit isn't a program; they are workouts of the day designed to elicit maximum carnage. Do not program these for your common client under any circumstances. While the brand has grown exponentially due to great marketing and a legion of loyal followers, it still has not addressed its number one flaw: the appropriateness of its programs for the individuals who participate. Mixing complexity with intensity is almost always a recipe for disaster, especially with new trainees or deconditioned individuals.

It's hard to criticize something that has already been criticized as much as CrossFit. That being said, we must make mention that designing WODs, or workouts of the day, for your clients does not make you a personal trainer.

Personal trainers design customized programs with built-in progression and regression for each client they work with. There isn't one workout that fits all. Elevate yourself above the noise and serve everyone as their own person.

CrossFit can still exist for what it is, but it shouldn't be infecting your programs or painting every canvas the same color.

April 21st

Consider the job and lifestyle of your client when designing your programs. If your client travels frequently, they'll likely tighten up after long flights and not be able to work as hard after they land. If they have a newborn at home, then they'll probably be lacking in sleep. Making day-to-day adjustments for your clients' lives is critical to the long-term success of any training program.

Your clients have twenty-three other hours in their day when they are not with you. This must always be taken into consideration when designing your exercise program, and more specifically, when you need to make day-to-day adaptations.

Expecting a client to crush an eight-by-eight of deadlifts after they've come home from a long business trip is a bit unreasonable. Modifying down in volume and intensity for one workout and letting them get back into the groove is more sensible.

Keep contact with your client's comings and goings and you'll be better able to serve them on a short-term basis, which has a tremendous impact on whether they'll stay with you longterm.

April 22nd

A program should have a certain level of flexibility built into it. Don't marry yourself to a specific piece of equipment. Be prepared with variations of your intended exercise in case your gym is busy. Familiarize yourself with the core elements of the movement pattern and not a specific exercise so that you can adjust if needed.

A program should be built around the major movement patterns and not a specific piece of equipment. Doing so allows for you to modify if the gym is crowded, your client isn't in an optimal training state, or you just want to switch things up a little.

For example, a client could be training a loaded horizontal push without specifically using the barbell bench press. You can use the barbell, dumbbells, bands, or a machine so long as you honor the goal of your program.

Over time, you'll find the exercises that work best for everyone in your roster, but initially, you'll want to keep all your options open. Remember, no one exercise is so superior to another that it *must* be done.

April 23rd

Push patterns are often less important than pull patterns in any training program. While this may sound crazy to the bench pressing, overhead pressing, push everything population of the world, it's true. Upper cross syndrome is becoming more common as people continue to hunch over in chairs for much of their day. It's important for a trainer to help a client retract and depress the scapulae, which improves posture, with additional pulling movements.

When programming for any client, aim to maintain a pull/push ratio of 2:1. There are reasons for this:

Numerous studies and a bevy of tremendous strength coaches have demonstrated that pulling more frequently is better for the shoulders, thoracic spine, and core.

Imagine that client with hunched over posture, the one who spends eight hours in a chair each day. Should they really be doing bench presses? Can they even benefit from the press if they are so internally rotated and flexed?

Pulling patterns should be a priority in all of your programs, but especially so in those with pre-existing issues with their shoulders, thoracic spine, and posture.

April 24th

Core stability patterns are the most important method of training the abdominals. Anti-movements such as planks, Pallof presses, rollouts, and loaded carries are far more important than crunches, leg raises, or bicycles. This is because the primary job of the core is to translate force between the limbs and resist forced movement of the spine. A great core can resist motion as well as create it.

In a world of magazine covers and Instagram models, it's easy to forget that the core is much more than the rectus-abdominus, aka the six-pack.

A trainer's job is to understand the function of the anatomy that we train. Regarding the core, this means that we must recognize that the core is a force transducer above all else. This fancy terminology points to the function of the core being to translate force to and from the limbs. It must be stable.

Training anti-flexion, anti-extension, anti-rotation, and anti-lateral flexion should be the primary method of core training in all your programs. The core must function well for the human body to perform at its best.

Everything else can be dotted into a program at a client's request.

April 25th

Programs should reflect a client's eating habits. A person will not be able to get stronger or induce hypertrophy on a low-calorie diet. Just the same, a client looking to lose weight must have a diet that reflects the intensity of their training program. A less intense program means lower caloric intake while a higher intensity program will require more fat or carbohydrates to support its intensity. Diet and exercise are not two separate topics. Rather, they are one interlinked strand.

It's popular in fitness writing to separate the topics of diet and exercise into two distinct tracks. Yet, when it comes to training clients, these two things are never separate. They are intertwined forever and always.

A client's eating habits will dramatically impact how they can train and vice versa.

For example, someone eating under maintenance calories will not be able to train nearly as heavy, nor as long, as they would with a caloric surplus. A training program must adapt to someone's current dietary habits.

Figure out what is most important, the intensity of exercise or the caloric intake of your client. Base everything else off this decision.

April 26th

When progressing a client's program, don't make wholesale changes. Adjust no more than three to four exercises while keeping most core principles the same. Change takes some time to take hold, so it's important to emphasize the same movement patterns, loads, and repetition schemes for an extended period. After twelve to sixteen weeks it's OK to begin changing the entire design of your program to reflect a different emphasis.

The idea of "muscle confusion" is one of the worst things to happen to the industry. While it's true that we should train the body with a variety of stimuli to promote growth and adaptation, it is important to note that we shouldn't be switching methods frequently.

You can't confuse a muscle, but you can leave the body in a state of overload where there are too many different stimuli to move in any specific direction.

Picture yourself standing at the center of the room and having multiple people call your name at once, each at different places of the room. You can't respond to everyone at once and so you freeze. This is not ideal for fitness.

April 27th

A primary movement can be matched with a core, a corrective, and a complimentary exercise to create a circuit that maximizes a client's time with you. Look to stack things together in logical ways that promote constant movement but don't compete with the effects of a primary movement. Each exercise has benefits on its own but putting them together dramatically increases the effect of the set without risking total breakdown.

The "art" of personal training boils down to the way we organize our programs and how we deliver the program to the client.

Following a proven structure, such as what is listed above, is one way to ensure that your art and science are working together.

A primary exercise is what causes the most significant challenge. The secondary presents a challenge that doesn't impact the primary movement, while the core and corrective address the client's ability to stabilize and mobilize.

For example, a heavier deadlift (say five repetitions) can be in a circuit with a plank hold for time, standing dumbbell overhead press, and a bird dog for time.

April 28th

You can only achieve so much at once. It's nearly impossible to gain muscle and train for a marathon at the same time. Instead, programming for two similar outcomes, such as gaining muscle and getting stronger, is your best bet. These two attributes work well together, and therefore, a training program can easily accommodate both.

Ensure your training programs are moving in a targeted direction. For example:

> Place a client's muscle-building efforts with strength training protocols and their higher calorie nutrition phases.

This organization ensures that all elements of a client's program are working in unison instead of against each other. This way they'll see greater results and they'll be happier with the job you've done as their professional.

It can be hard to resist the temptation to conquer the world in just one program, but you must stay strong and observe the laws of science.

Coach your clients to trust the process and follow your lead. Adherence to your protocol will increase when your clients know there is a "why" behind the order and methods.

April 29th

A program must consider the effects of itself. You can't put a heavy squat day after a heavy deadlift day and expect good results. Temper your load and intensity in the movements and provide time for recovery. This doesn't mean that you can't train these patterns on back-to-back days though, as a great coach can use the tightness from a heavy squat to help cue better tension in a lighter hinge pattern on the following day.

A great coach is one who can design a program that has the future in mind while still respecting the effects of the past and present. This is apparent in how a trainer organizes the volume and intensity in their program.

Be mindful of the effects of each individual workout on your client and organize exercises and loads appropriately.

Building your programs to train each movement pattern multiple times a week is the building block to great training success but also requires you to "wave" your loads and volume throughout the week.

Study periodization and master this art.

April 30th

*Your hidden variable can be rest. Less rest increases
cardiovascular output and decreases strength, while
the opposite is true of more rest. Study the concepts
of fiber types, rest intervals, and metabolic pathways
and utilize this information to keep your client
training in the zone you want.*

You can only push the human body so hard before it
pushes back. As professionals, we know not to push
our clients so hard that their health is at risk, but this
extends much further.

The ability to adapt to a stimulus, or training stress,
depends on having the proper amount of rest. This
applies to both in-session rest and time between
workouts.

For example, a person training to get stronger must
take longer rest periods when working with heavy
loads near their max. At the opposite end, a triathlete
must decrease their rest periods and lower their loads
to mimic the stress of competition.

Rest is a major variable that can impact the intensity and
results of your training program.

May

Resistance Training

"The world's favorite season is the spring. All things seem possible in May."

—Edwin Way Teale

"The resistance that you fight physically in the gym and the resistance that you fight in life can only build a strong character."

—Arnold Schwarzenegger

May 1st

*Load is the most impactful variable in resistance training.
How much load is applied to an exercise dictates
everything from how many repetitions a person will
complete, whether the form breaks down, and how much
volume you'll apply over the course of the session.
Overloading is never wise and underloading may rob
someone of the appropriate stimulus. Always take the time
to fine-tune your load prescriptions.*

Think of how easily your body can drop down into a full-depth squat when you are dealing only with your bodyweight.

Now, ask yourself if you'll be able to handle the same depth with a barbell on your back or a dumbbell in your hand. More importantly, ask if you *should* be working toward that depth (under load) in the first place.

Realize that the weights you prescribe have the power to make or break your client, their workout, and even their perception of exercise.

Take an extra moment and ensure your client is about to work with an appropriate load.

May 2nd

Taking the time to master a movement pattern, say a hinge, is imperative to training a loaded exercise. A deadlift will only be as good as a person's hinge pattern. Far too many coaches are in such a rush to deliver results to a client that they overlook the importance of movement quality. Much like someone learns words by first learning letters, it's important to master the movements before worrying about loaded exercise.

Mastery of movement patterns is a goal that far too many individuals overlook en route to getting in shape, building muscle, and burning fat.

Your job as a professional is to coach clients to perform exercises with the best quality. Our pledge to do no harm must always be in the forefront of our mind.

What may excite your clients more is that exercises done correctly are more likely to generate the results they seek. A finely-tuned deadlift done with the right load will always create more positive change than one done with poor form and an incorrect load.

Coach quality: it is the building block of all that you do, will do, and will be known for.

May 3rd

The body is its own resistance. Do not discount this fact when you observe a client exercise. Some people will lack the strength to manage their own body in space and shouldn't be asked to do compound movements until they are ready. Taking the time to strengthen the body against its own resistance is an often skipped but never regretted step.

In the rush to get results in your local gym, with all its amenities, it's easy to skip past bodyweight workouts and onto the equipment that surrounds you.

There's obviously nothing wrong with machines or external resistance (it's the backbone of a great program), but we should never overlook the benefits of bodyweight movements.

You can use bodyweight exercises to build strength, such as with traditional push-ups, squats, and pull-ups. Or, incorporate flow movements such as Animal Flow, yoga, or martial arts into your client's programs to help them discover new ranges of motion. You can even include your correctives and activations in this category too.

May 4th

*A free weight always responds to gravity. In other words,
it wants to move in a straight line toward the floor, which
differs from a load on a pulley system. Knowing this
difference is key because a coach must ensure that a load is
placed over the body correctly or that the body is in the
proper position over the weight to optimally and safely
overcome its resistance.*

Not all weight acts the same, especially in the modern
fitness facility. Dumbbells and barbells respond to
gravity, a vertical force, whereas pulleys "resist" in
whatever plane you place them.

This is a critical concept to grasp to make sure that you
safely load each client uniquely to their body structure,
capacity, and goals.

Performing a dumbbell chest press will have a different
set of rules than will a standing cable chest press. The
path of the resistance, the angle of the starting position,
and the load itself are going to be dictated by varying
the force profile.

Play with these resistances in your own time and
feel how they act differently against your body. Your
personal experience, when paired with a biomechanics
lecture or two, will help you coach this concept and
guide clients to results.

May 5th

Heavy loads require much more preparation than lighter loads. Be sure to progress clients through a variety of loads as you build toward the optimal training weight. It is important to not rush preparation for safety and performance purposes. You don't want someone going for a near max effort lift while they still feel cold or disconnected from their body.

We've all heard the stories about the guy who can walk into the gym, cold, and lift some absurd amount of weight off the floor as if it were nothing.

Well, your clients are not going to be that guy (or girl) and it's important for you to understand that before loading up any barbells for them.

Beyond the safety factor, it is known science that the body works much better when muscles are activated, blood is flowing, body temperature is elevated, and the brain and body are having a conversation.

So, always load your clients gradually as you work toward any heavy lifts. Prepare their body for the tasks ahead by engaging the neurological system in advance of their primary movements.

May 6th

Utilizing lighter loads and higher repetitions is for more than just endurance and fatigue work. Recent science has shown that type I muscle fibers, those capable of high endurance and low force output, are also capable of hypertrophy (muscle growth). While their total growth potential is less than that of type II fibers, the potential is still there. Utilize lighter loads with a slower tempo to maximize this effect.

Trainers and trainees alike can agree that lighter loads and higher repetitions are for training the endurance capacity of a muscle, otherwise known as the type I muscle fiber.

What's impressive though is that these fatigue-resistant fibers can also grow like their type II partners. Sure, their rate of growth and response is not of the same magnitude as the explosive fibers, but it's still there.

This scientific discovery should make you feel more confident in programming higher repetition exercises into your programs, especially for individuals looking to achieve hypertrophy as a training goal.

May 7th

Repetition ranges are not just arbitrary numbers thrown into the training space to organize our workouts. Each repetition range will be dictated by the load applied to the body and the tempo of movement. The result of this will impact which muscle fibers fire, which metabolic pathway is most utilized, and the overall training effect.

The classic prescription of "three sets of ten" is one of the worst things to happen to the fitness world. It convinced everyone that "ten" was some magic number for fitness.

Science, thankfully, has shown that specific repetition ranges are most effective for specific loads, which correlate to specific adaptations in our body.

- Lifting loads for three to five repetitions will improve strength output over time
- Lifting moderate loads for six to twelve repetitions can influence hypertrophy
- Anything over twelve repetitions is typically for endurance training

This science is mandatory learning for any fitness professional looking to deliver results to their clients.

May 8th

*Type II fibers are split into two categories. Type IIb fibers
are recruited in those maximum or near maximum efforts,
while the type IIa fibers tend to make their appearance known
in the six to ten repetition range. The difference between
these fibers doesn't matter as much to the common client
but would matter to someone who is training for power,
absolute strength, or hypertrophy.*

The nerdy side of this profession typically means
nothing to our paying clients. They don't concern
themselves with the details.

Understanding the subtleties of fiber types is one
example of these nerdy details. Our type II fibers are
commonly known as our force-producing, growth
fibers. This is entirely true, but lacking specificity.

Type IIa fibers are sort of "dream" fibers in the sense
that they have better resistance to fatigue than IIb fibers
but can produce similar levels of force. IIb fibers do have
a higher potential for output though, to be clear.

These fibers always fire together, but using specific
loads, speeds, or repetition ranges will create a greater
response in one or the other.

May 9th

Compound movements should be the primary exercise in your training sessions. These multi-joint, typically loaded, and highly technical movements should be done early in a program to ensure optimal performance. There are exceptions, such as individuals returning from injury, populations with neurological conditions, and elite athletes.

Compound exercises, such as the deadlift, squat, power clean, overhead press, and row are the foundation of any great resistance training program.

Each client you train may see a different variation of these key movements, but the pattern should still be present in their program.

Compound movements recruit more muscle mass, can be loaded a bit heavier, and burn more calories while also integrating the entire body into a singular unit, which is a more effective way of achieving true fitness.

These are the patterns that can cause the most change in your clients due to their muscular, metabolic, and neurological demand. They must be a priority in most of your training programs.

May 10th

Rest is an important variable when we discuss strength training Recovery is imperative for optimal performance under load. More rest is required for heavy loads (two to four minutes) while lighter loads can use shorter rest periods (thirty seconds to one minute). There is some wiggle room depending upon a client's capacity though.

People often refer to the human body as a machine. In many ways, the body is a machine: a highly effective mechanism capable of doing and learning an extraordinary number of things.

However, unlike a mechanical system, the human body is made up of biological cells, which require adequate fuel and recovery to continue operating.

The scientific principles of rest must be considered when designing and executing your program. Too much and too little rest both have negative effects upon your clients.

The metabolic demand of an exercise changes as the load increases. This directly corelates with the need for additional rest as more ATP is expended during a near max effort than during a less intense effort.

A trainer must honor these "laws" to be successful.

May 11th

Carbohydrates are critical for force development and strength training. Your client will see decreased strength output if they are trying to limit the amount of carbohydrates in their diet. Adjust the loads and total volume of a program for someone who is in this situation. It's about maximizing quality and not quantity with a dieting client.

The years will pass and still there will be a popular diet that dramatically limits carbohydrates. And so long as you are a trainer, you will have clients inquiring about these widespread dieting fads.

When training a client who is looking to get stronger, build muscle, or achieve a specific performance outcome, you must know that you can't achieve those ends without adequate fuel, specifically carbohydrates.

As the primary driver of ATP in muscles, carbohydrates are critical for rapid energy repletion: a necessary physiological process for heavy lifts or highly intense bouts of exercise.

You can't expect quick recovery times between sets in a client who lacks the necessary nutrients for ATP repletion.

May 12th

Tempo is an underrated variable for increasing the intensity of a given exercise. Taking the time to slow down the eccentric and/or the concentric phase of a movement will increase the time under tension and provide a greater stimulus for change. Adding in a static isometric at the change-over point of an exercise can also greatly increase intensity without adding load.

One of the best ways to increase a person's chance of building muscle is to increase the time their muscles spend "under tension."

This method aims to maximize the amount of time working muscles are exposed to load and stress to trigger a hypertrophic response in the working tissue. More work requires more recovery.

You'll want to expose your clients to a tempo slowed to two or three seconds in both concentric and eccentric phases. This timing, in conjunction with adequate load, can stimulate the body to grow muscle cells.

***This method of training is not appropriate for clients with health conditions or injuries to the training area. ***

Day by Day

May 13th

Testosterone is critical for muscle growth, but don't underestimate the ability of the female body to build muscle even though it doesn't have as much of the muscle-building hormone. Realize that the female body is capable of training harder and more frequently than the male body. With women, training more frequently with submaximal loads is the recipe for successful strength and muscle building.

The endocrine system, where hormones are in play, is a major key to someone's success and failure in their fitness endeavors. For example, the hormone testosterone aids in building muscle and burning fat cells in the body. This is the male sex hormone.

Yet, science has demonstrated that training frequently with sub-maximal loads can trigger similar responses in women. While the average female has significantly less testosterone in her body than the average male, she can still trigger hypertrophy and strength adaptations with the appropriate training.

Other hormones will come into play and the adaptations will still take place if the program is created correctly. Research these phenomena and implement modalities in your programs to trigger change.

May 14th

Limb length is a major factor. Longer limbs increase the distance a resistance must travel and so the individual does more total work. This increased work load will make it harder for a client to achieve elite strength numbers on pressing and squatting movements but may give them an advantage in power movements such as jumping and throwing.

Watch a professional basketball player squat and this tip will immediately resonate with you. Soon after, watch a barely five-foot person squat and you'll be blown away by the difference.

A person's limb length is a critical factor in their ability to perform an exercise well. Every exercise, or movement pattern, is available to all people of all heights, as long as you adjust the demands to meet them where they are.

A tall individual may deadlift from elevated blocks for the entirety of their lives. This doesn't mean they are weak—it just fits them better. In a similar way, a shorter person may never jump onto a high box because they just can't tuck their knees and get enough lift.

We all have advantages and disadvantages.

🏋

May 15th

The length of someone's segments (femur, shins, torso, arms) is going to dictate which position is best for deadlifting (when discussing the barbell variety). The relationship with the barbell can change dramatically when one or more segments are shorter or longer than "normal." Studying the biomechanics of the deadlift is key to always putting clients in the right position.

The deadlift is a movement that puts the body at tremendous risk of injury due to the need to overcome inertia when lifting the bar off the floor. This lack of a stretch reflex (as found in the bottom of a squat or bench press) means that a person must be in perfect position to safely, and successfully, lift a weight from the floor.

A person's leg and arm segments are factors that will dictate position (and potentially eliminate positions). Look at your clients to assess which positions they'll be able to create the most strength in (safely) for their body type.

You may need to change foot and/or hand position to help a client perform the lift optimally. Both factors will impact hip position and knee flexion, two critical elements of a successful deadlift.

May 16th

Rotational core work should be taught as an entire spinal and hip movement first and isolated spinal rotation second. Isolating one section of the spine (when loaded) is a recipe for disaster for people who aren't in tune with their core. Rotation should involve the hips, like a golf swing, to protect the lumbar and cervical spines from too much torque. Only once a client demonstrates mastery of a full rotation should you consider segmental rotations.

The spine can deal with rotational forces, but it shouldn't do so on a regular basis. Instead, teaching a client proper mechanics of hip, torso, and shoulder rotation is critical to avoiding injury and maximizing rotational force production.

A client should be taught how to rotate from the toe of their back foot through the leg, with the pelvis, through the torso and finally with the thoracic spine.

Segmental forces, such as those seen in woodchop exercises, are fine if the load is light and the client is ready for such specificity (and can demonstrate control over tempo).

Most individuals will, and should, emphasize getting their entire body into a turn.

May 17th

Overhead pressing isn't just difficult due to the high possibility of shoulder impingement or weak rotator cuff muscles; it is also tough because it requires the abdominal wall to contract and keep the lumbar spine from overarching. Focus on this detail when coaching a client to see better results and a healthier spine.

The overhead push has more qualifications than any other movement pattern before it can be added into a client's program. Unlike movements such as the hinge, squat, or horizontal pull, there aren't that many ways to regress an overhead pressing pattern to help a client who has difficulties or limitations.

One of those places where a problem could arise is in the core. Many times, a person goes into extreme lumbar arching (especially with heavy loads) to "get under" the weight. The arch, if left unchecked, could cause significant pain and damage to the spinal discs.

This breakdown in form also causes the pectoral muscles to engage, which steals away focus from the shoulder and upper back musculature, which is the real target. Mastering position at a load should be a prerequisite before going heavier.

May 18th

Bench pressing is best performed with dumbbells for most clients. The barbell can lock someone's shoulders into a poor position that may not be ready for, does not allow for a great stretch at the bottom, and could be intimidating to someone uncomfortable in the gym. Dumbbells, however, boost unilateral strength, allow for multiple hand positions, and seem easier to someone unfamiliar with weight training.

If you were asked to close your eyes and begin describing what you see when you walk into your favorite gym, it wouldn't take very long to get to the crowd of individuals who use the barbell flat bench press in their workouts.

There is nothing inherently wrong with using the barbell bench in a program. It is, after all, an elite builder of pushing strength. However, as a personal trainer, your job is to always do what is best for *the client*.

Most individuals you'll train will benefit from the added range of motion, increased neuromuscular demand, and elimination of "locking" in the motion that dumbbells provide. As always your job is to match the exercise to the client and not the other way around.

May 19th

Posture exercises should be in every workout for every client. Some will need more work, and others will need less. However, movements like face pulls, pullovers, planks, glute bridges, and the variety of thoracic mobility exercises should be in all programs. A person can only be as good as their standard posture allows them to be.

There is no exercise program that can succeed without addressing the muscles of the core and posterior chain. These regions are the cornerstone of human functional movement and athleticism.

As a professional, you are being paid to address the big rocks, not just to move the small ones down the stream. A person's posture and the impact it has on so many other aspects of health and wellness is one of the biggest rocks you are responsible for.

Always look to train the muscles that control rib flare, keep the pelvis *mostly* neutral at rest, pull the scapulae down and back, and help keep the natural curvature of the spine in a static position. This is a must for all clients no matter how talented they are at a given sport, lift, or modality.

Everyone's home should be taken care of before they travel.

May 20th

Post-activation potentiation is a great trick to increase someone's power output. Using sprints or vertical jumps can cause a tremendous spark to someone's squat or deadlift. Similar effects have been seen in reverse too. Try using broad jumps before a deadlift and watch your client explode with the weight. Just the same, a set of heavy deadlifts may help someone jump even further than they expected.

Advanced training tactics should always be saved for those who are ready for the stress it puts on the body, so be wise when you employ post-activation potentiation with a client.

That being said, its effects on performance are well-documented in the scientific literature and testimonials from the field.

Your client's ability to generate high levels of force, whether it is absolute strength or fast twitch power, is often dependent upon their environment prior to the demand.

Employing a plyometric before a high-load lift can trick the body into firing more fibers more frequently to get the job done.

May 21st

Age doesn't preclude someone from lifting weights. There may be a "too young" but there isn't a "too old." Tailor the load to your client and don't overshoot. Resistance training is important for the aging population because it strengthens bones and muscles while maintaining coordination. The loss of muscle mass is one of the major causes of inactivity in older populations, so resistance training is a critical element of any senior fitness plan.

For many years, it was reported that lifting weights was a dangerous, unnecessary, and even unhealthy form of exercise for growing teenagers, pregnant women, and elderly individuals alike.

Thankfully, science has kicked silly information like that out of the window in favor of proof that it is one of the best forms of exercise for anyone, of any age, so long as the person making the prescriptions is customizing it to the individual.

As a coach, your job is to intelligently add load to your clients and always ask yourself why you are choosing a specific weight or movement.

No matter who you train, be wise with your load prescriptions. Ask *"is this appropriate for this person?"*

May 22nd

Know the difference between power and strength. While it may sound like semantics, being able to explain the difference adds to your credibility. A power exercise shouldn't be done with maximal load since velocity is a major element of this movement. Strength exercises, on the other hand, will have a much lower velocity but a significantly higher load.

Tell a person on the street that you want to make them strong and powerful and they'll think those two words mean the same thing.

But as a coach, you should know the difference and be able to comfortably explain it to your clients when you discuss the choices you make with their training program. It all comes down to force versus time.

Picture the big guy at a powerlifting meet slowly pressing a loaded bar off his chest with a load that looks like it could crush him; that's strength.

That Olympic lifter who quickly clean and jerked 300 pounds; that's power, the expression of force against time.

Both have their place in a program, so long as you know which is which and when to employ them.

Day by Day

May 23rd

Explosive movements such as box jumps or medicine ball throws are a great way to train a person's power. They also have a high metabolic demand. However, be sure your client is ready for this sort of impact before implementing. Just because box jumps are "hard" doesn't mean every client should doing them. There is a lot of risk.

Every single individual you train should have power addressed in their program, but it's crucial to remember that those power exercises must be appropriate for their age, physical condition, and goals.

Having an older client do an intense explosive movement, such as a box jump, just because box jumps are hard, and it'd be cool if she could, is not a valid justification for the stress this exercise places on her body.

However, having that same client do a less stressful power exercise, such as a medicine ball chop throw since she enjoys playing tennis on the weekends, is both safe and appropriate. Be smart with your power prescriptions.

The forces in play during acceleration and negative acceleration must be known, at least conceptually.

May 24th

Resistance training for the core requires understanding the limitations of the segments of the spine. We must minimize lumbar flexion and rotation, as well as thoracic flexion. Similarly, we shouldn't have much lateral flexion into our programs. It is better to load a stability pattern, such as a plank, than to add weight to a crunch. The core is meant to stabilize and transduce forces.

Far too often, trainers advance core exercises like they do with other movements, adding load or intensity once it gets less challenging.

Here is the thing though: adding load does not necessarily make a core exercise better since its primary function is to *transduce* forces. The core functions to stabilize the center of the body as the limbs translate force into the world around it.

Going heavier in a wood chop or a crunch has a greater risk of injury than it does reward once you pass a certain threshold. More importantly, we need to minimize our exposure to extreme ranges of motion within the spine to avoid injury and keep our body performing well.

May 25th

Unilateral training is an integral part of helping your client build their best body. By individualizing the limbs and forcing the body to overcome imbalances and navigate stability, you'll make the whole much greater. Using single-sided exercises to prepare for heavier bilateral lifts is an effective way to elicit more strength in some clients.

All too often, trainers stay focused on bilateral movements to drive up lift totals and (in theory) increase the stress of the workout. Their thought is that this will lead to the best results.

Meanwhile, the best coaches have long since realized that single leg or single arm training can dramatically improve strength and stability while improving the foundation for hypertrophy and endurance goals.

They take the time to improve each part of the body to increase total strength once they return their client to bilateral movements.

An example of this would be to use Bulgarian split squats to improve a client's ability to better squat with both feet on the ground.

May 26th

*There is nothing wrong with training the "glamour"
muscles with additional volume. If a client wants to see
notable change in a specific area, then it is your job to
get them there. However, prioritize this work after
you've nailed down your major primary movements
and emphasized quality.*

You might think this book is against training a client on anything glamorous. The word function is used far more than glamour, after all.

You should absolutely train the muscles that your clients want to see improved on their bodies, and you should absolutely spend time working toward their aesthetic goals.

The key is to prioritize them after the big rocks of your session: function, movement quality, strength development, etc. A great coach can give a client what they want and what they need without having to negotiate with them.

For glamour, have a plan to throw a lot of training volume at specific muscles after you've achieved your major goals for the day. Feel free to push someone to muscular fatigue after they've addressed their movement patterns that session.

Day by Day

May 27th

*Accessory movements are the flare of a program. There
is only so much variation you'll need with your major
movements, and so the spice of your "dish" will come
from the unique exercises that you round out circuits,
sets, and sessions with. Show your character but always
respect the rules of exercise science.*

A successful exercise program is one that emphasizes
moving the big rocks first and foremost. This is done
by putting the bulk of effort into major compound
movements such as the hinge, squat, and pulling patterns.

From there, you'll make decisions about what your
client needs and wants:

- **Needs** (correctives, core, and conditioning)
- **Wants** (specific body part development)

It is during accessory movements, those additional
exercises that surround your core focuses in an exercise
program, that you can add some flare and excitement to
your program.

With everything else though, stick to what works, what
is safe, and what can be coached effectively.

May 28th

The neural load of resistance training must be accounted for. Even if muscles don't "feel" sore, there is a high probability that the central nervous system and the peripheral nervous system are worn down. You'll see it in your client's ability to retain focus and perform exercises correctly. Training experience greatly impacts neural fatigue but doesn't eliminate it.

Resistance training is known most for its ability to break down muscle tissue and burn calories, but people often overlook the effect it has on the neurological system of the body.

Training with weights requires the body to coordinate movement up and down the nervous system (afferent and efferent communication). This stress can be quite great and require multiple days of recovery before someone feels capable of pushing hard again.

Yet, in a fitness economy where soreness is the goal, most people overlook the effects on the nervous system in favor of training again. A great coach accounts for this in their training and builds in adequate rest and regeneration techniques to avoid neural fatigue.

May 29th

The landmine device may be on the of the best implements in the gym. Even if you are simply pushing a barbell into the corner of a wall, this angle allows for incredible training to occur. A safe variation of pressing, squatting, and even deadlifting is possible with the landmine. Consider adding it into all your training programs.

The irony of modern fitness facilities is that some of the best modalities are the oldest and least fancy. In a space full of thousand-dollar equipment, jamming a barbell into a corner and putting a plate on one side still has tremendous value.

As a coach, utilizing the landmine device allows for you to accomplish two things:

1. Load the body in a unique angle to jumpstart advancements in performance, and
2. Defer load away from gravity to help someone go from unloaded to loaded exercise modalities.

This versatility allows for you to train a wide variety of individuals with it. This could save your facility precious capital and allow you to streamline the training process for all clients.

May 30th

Remember that the best resistance exercise is the one that fits your client's current body and goals. Not everyone needs to touch a barbell and not everyone needs to go heavy. Just the same, pay attention to what clients already do for their body and look to provide the stimulus that they are missing.

As coaches, we all have our preferences with exercise. Some of us love to use kettlebells to push our bodies to new levels of fitness and performance. Others find success with barbells, resistance bands, unloaded movement, and even fixed machines. Yet, none of these modalities is superior to the next.

When training a client, it is crucial to see the gap between our preferences and their needs. Each of the exercises, and the way we do them, should be unique to the individual who is being trained. There is no one-size-fits-all in personal training.

Always load your clients with what works for them and not with some "ideal" modality that worked for you or for others. You'll be better off and so will they.

Unique is the word of the day.

Day by Day

☕

May 31st

The eccentric portion of an exercise does the most cellular damage to working muscles (due to the breaking of myosin/actin cross bridges). It is also the portion of an exercise that many clients rush through to start the next repetition. Always coach your clients to slowly extend their joints, lower the load, and control their descent.

Form and tempo should be the primary focuses of a trainer when observing a client exercise. While it can be tempting to count repetition or provide positive reinforcement, the most critical things you can do are:

1. Make sure they are putting their body in the best possible position to successfully complete the exercise, and
2. Make sure they are managing their concentric, isometric, and eccentric tempos to elicit better results and protect themselves against injury.

The last point, tempo, is critical since many injuries come from the rapid deceleration of the body or an external load.

A great coach ensures that a client takes their time completing the eccentric portion of a lift.

June

Cardiovascular Training

"How did it get so late so soon? It's night before it's afternoon. December is here before it's June. My goodness how the time has flewn. How did it get so late so soon?"

—Dr. Seuss

"The reason I exercise is for the quality of life I enjoy."

—Kenneth H. Cooper

June 1st

Cardiovascular function is one of the most important aspects of health. A healthy heart, lungs, and blood vessels make every other aspect of fitness easier to handle and improve the quality of life overall. There is no client who should ever skip cardiovascular training completely.

For years in the fitness industry, the adage that people should avoid cardiovascular exercise and just "lift weights faster" has both helped and hurt many bodies.

First, it isn't wrong that people should be lifting weights and focusing on strength training if they want to see their bodies change shape and become more defined.

Where this advice misses the mark is that it misidentifies the purpose of cardiovascular training. It's about much more than losing weight or burning calories.

Cardio improves the function of the heart, lungs, and the entire vascular system. It helps improve blood flow to working muscles, can decrease cortisol levels, and improve sleep. As coaches, we must ensure our clients do cardio.

June 2nd

A cardiovascular exercise plan needs to account for what a client needs and is willing to commit the time to. Providing blanket cardio for everyone isn't the best solution. Think about what each person might need and how they can successfully fit it into their daily schedules. The busier the person, the harder it will be. Go for short and simple as your starting block.

It is most important to be realistic with your clients when you prescribe their cardiovascular routine. Far too often as coaches, we push what is shown to provide the best results instead of what will work for our client in the here and now.

So, instead of prescribing the standard thirty minutes three days per week for each client you work with, focus on customizing their plan to their current capabilities.

It will be tremendously hard to get someone who doesn't do cardio currently to commit to a demanding (in their eyes) plan right away. Instead, start with multiple bouts of ten minutes or just one day of the standard thirty minutes.

June 3rd

Carbohydrates are critical fuel for shorter bouts of cardio, such as intervals. Meanwhile, dietary fats are what sustain long distances or durations. Be sure clients are consuming the right type of calories to fuel their exercise.

Once again, we must revisit the idea that our nutrition and training are not separate issues. Rather, they are highly intertwined and often dependent upon each other.

In the case of cardiovascular exercise, it is imperative to tie the primary energy calorie to the mode in which someone is training.

Carbohydrates and fats are important for all populations, although training duration and intensity have a dramatic impact on which macronutrient becomes the primary source of energy.

Shorter, more intense bouts of exercise rely on carbohydrates to provide the glucose and ATP necessary to perform. Meanwhile, longer bouts are reliant on fats to fuel the lower intensity muscle contractions.

Food is fuel for training.

June 4ᵗʰ

*Running isn't an activity that should be done by everyone.
In fact, many people haven't been taught how to run
properly. It isn't as simple as putting one foot in front of
the other. The running stride is highly complex and requires
assessment and coaching. Take the time to reconstruct a
person's stride prior to prescribing long distances or intense
sprints. Just the same, be wary of asking an overweight client
to run to lose weight. The impact on their joints will be much
greater than someone who is already fit.*

The stress created by running must always be considered
when prescribing it as an exercise modality. As a coach,
you must ask yourself the following question:

Is my client capable of running without getting hurt by the repetitive impact?

Most people will fail this litmus test and will need
coaching from you, corrective exercises to address
structural issues, or they'll need to lose weight prior to
beginning their program to decrease the stress of the
run.

People must be fit to run and not run to be fit.

June 5th

Prescribe shorter bouts of cardio to help clients create the habit of doing it on their own. Sure, ten minutes isn't going to change the world, but it can be enough to start a new habit if done consistently. Asking for a series of long duration cardio too early may push a client away or make success harder to achieve. Remember, we want progress over perfection.

Something done consistently becomes habit and habits become the foundation of who we are as individuals. If you wake up early each day for a light exercise, a peaceful cup of coffee, and a homemade breakfast, then chances are you are a person who values their health and happiness.

With that said, it is important to help clients get into the habit of exercise prior to increasing the intensity of it. Beginning someone with frequent, short duration cardiovascular work is often the best method for getting adherence to a cardio training plan.

Start slow and allow the client to build confidence in themselves and your program before asking them to do much harder things.

June 6th

You should know how it feels to do the intervals you prescribe for your clients. If you, the coach, struggle, maybe it's too much to ask of your clients. Always understand the demands of your programming and be sure that a "fit" individual can handle it before handing it off to someone who is trusting you to keep them safe.

Trainers should always know how it feels to do the workouts they are prescribing for their clients, but this is especially true when we look at interval cardiovascular exercise.

Often, a client is pushed far beyond their capacity because a trainer simply jotted down a ratio of work to rest for them to follow without considering just how hard that would be to maintain for a "fit" person.

A responsible coach tests their own prescriptions and ensures that they adjust up and down for each client.

This is analogous to a chef tasting a small portion of a meal to be certain it's the cooked the right way. Verify the quality of your work before passing it on to the customer.

June 7th

All intervals should be prescribed in the form of work-to-rest ratios. Studies have shown that doing anything more intense than 1:1 (equal work to rest) is not beneficial to the exerciser. Use 1:1 as your ideal and work backward from there. Many beginners will need more rest, so ratios such as 1:3 or 1:5 are appropriate. The key is to allow enough rest for optimal performance to occur during each interval.

Prescribing intervals for a client, whether they be aerobic or anaerobic in nature, must respect a client's current fitness level.

With a work-to-rest ratio, it is important to start with too much rest and progress until a person is challenged to work through fatigue. Many clients may never surpass a 1:2 ratio (in which you rest twice as much as you work, such as 10 seconds on and 20 seconds off). This is perfectly fine and will still be a challenge for most people.

What we must never do is provide less rest than work for our clients. Our job is to make our clients better and not run them into the ground. Choosing appropriate intervals is a major factor in deciding what you do.

June 8th

Hydration is a critical element of cardiovascular performance. Be sure to preload your client's cardiovascular program with at least six to ten ounces of water before starting. Clients may sip throughout the period of exercise but shouldn't be consuming too much water while working to prevent cramping. Water is most important before and after exercise.

Water is the foundation of all living things. It's why we coach clients to drink more of the clear liquid.

We often misunderstand the way water works in the body during exercise. The body pulls most of its blood flow to the cardiovascular system and working muscles during exercise, leaving very little in the digestive system. This can make it hard to absorb water during an intense bout of exercise.

Therefore, coaching clients to preload before intense cardio and reload after is critical to enhancing their performance without risking cramping or G.I. discomfort. Tell clients to "sip" during exercise.

Then, after exercise, they should be replenishing as much as they can (within their own comfort levels). Water, carbohydrates, and protein are best.

June 9th

Sports are excellent for cardiovascular exercise. A competitive game of tennis burns more calories than does a run on a treadmill. So, don't take away the fun your clients have with sports in favor of a boring treadmill run. Instead, push the client to play their favorite sport more often. They'll get a great workout and continue to develop their skills at something they are passionate about.

It is important to remember that our clients are people with likes and dislikes, needs and wants, and opinions galore. This fact should always guide our coaching methods when we prescribe cardiovascular exercise to our clients.

For example, a client who loves playing tennis or competes in a basketball league should not be told to skip their passion for something as boring and repetitive as running on a treadmill.

Instead, coach them to play harder and push themselves into a zone where their body is working hard to keep up. Your job as a coach is to make someone better at the life they want to live and not one you want to push on them.

June 10ᵗʰ

There is value in a long walk no matter what shape a client is in. Taking an hour-long stroll is great for the metabolism, boosts the feel-good hormones, and can help boost brain function and problem-solving ability.

The industry has gone too far by ostracizing anything that doesn't make you sweat profusely or push you so hard that you question your life decisions.

When talking with clients, especially those who aren't avid fans of exercise, it is important to acknowledge the benefits of a long stroll around the neighborhood.

While this type of exercise isn't going to catapult anyone to the cover of a fitness magazine, a long walk will increase the metabolic rate, release hormones like dopamine, and help people problem-solve and think critically.

Once again, your goal as a coach is to meet people where they are and slowly move them toward where they need to be. A sixty-minute walk is a great starting point, and even a great reset button, for your training clients.

June 11th

Most modern cardiovascular machines have televisions now. This is fine, but be sure to coach your clients to be mindful of their posture while moving. Many people will push their head forward to see the TV better as they walk/ride/glide. Also, be sure that your clients understand that the priority is exercise, not the television. Intensity needs to be high enough to elicit change.

We can't fight technological progress even when we disagree with its implementation. So, when prescribing gym-based cardiovascular exercise to your clients, like an elliptical or treadmill, know that they'll have the TV on.

Most clients, and even trainers, need something to entertain their minds while they plod through a methodical cardio workout. The problem is that most people zone out on what they are watching and keep their legs pumping but forget completely about their posture.

This is where you come in. Instead of coaching your clients to exercise without the TV, know that it will be on and focus your coaching efforts on how to maintain posture throughout.

June 12th

Fun always has a place in fitness. Don't force a client to do the stair master just because you know it's a hard workout. Some people love spin classes, Zumba classes, or Tabata-style classes, so let them enjoy themselves. Let your client enjoy their journey. Compliance is always easier to achieve when the individual is enjoying the process.

In a society where most workout shirts say "no pain, no gain" or "sweat is fat crying," it's easy to convince someone that exercise isn't meant to be enjoyable.

This is a problem in and of itself. Exercise can absolutely be an enjoyable experience, especially if we as trainers prescribe things that our clients like. Sure, the whole program won't be a party, but that doesn't mean that one day each week can't be a reprieve from the regularity of a great program.

Whether they take a spin class, dance in Zumba, or play sports, never deny a client a chance to exercise in a manner that they enjoy. As a trainer, you have no professional right to rob someone of happiness, period.

June 13th

*Some studies have shown that even fifteen minutes of
cardiovascular exercise is enough to push off feelings of anxiety
and depression. These conditions likely impact many of your
clients, so be sure to encourage them to take a walk,
a jog, or ride their bike when they need a morale boost.*

In an ever-changing world full of online social interaction, constant pressure to live a good life, and the stress of survival, anxiety and depression are common afflictions.

A great coach understands that sometimes our brains and our bodies don't communicate well. Even more importantly, sometimes our brains play games on us, manipulate us, and even fail us.

A client who struggles with anxiety or depression often finds that even small doses of cardiovascular exercise help them cope and think clearly. The increase in blood flow to brain tissue, the uptick in metabolic rate, and the flow of dopamine are crucial to a person's well-being.

Often, all you need to do to be adored by your clients is to be there for them when they need it most.

June 14th

Fasted cardio is a popular modality for fat loss in the physique community, but few studies have shown that it's any better than doing cardio later in the day or after a meal. While it may seem logical to push the body without fuel (thus burning fat), there are more risks than rewards, which makes it unprofessional to recommend.

This is a tip that is sure to challenge the ethos of many physique coaches in the industry, but this point must be made to protect clients from damaging their metabolism.

Fasted cardio is used to force the body to burn stored fats as energy since the digestive system is empty and incapable of providing blood sugar from newly consumed foods. This sounds great in principle, but for most trainees it is grossly inappropriate for their body type.

Most clients aren't that advanced, nor do they need such radical measures. The body breaks down proteins with fats in a fasted state, which could lower their basal metabolic rate over time, ultimately damaging them. You must ask yourself *"do the negatives outweigh positives here?"* For most of your clients the answer is going to be absolutely yes.

🔔

June 15th

*Cardiovascular exercise shouldn't be used for "fat-burning"
in the first place. Quality nutrition, a sound lifting
program, and great sleep are the backbones of losing body
fat. Cardiovascular exercise does contribute to caloric
expenditure, but improving heart and lung function
is its primary benefit.*

While cardiovascular exercise does boost caloric expenditure, and can increase lipolysis (fat burning), it shouldn't be used only for this purpose.

The fitness industry and its profitable obsession with body image has made cardio "useless" unless you are trying to be super lean and show off your body.

Nonsense! Cardiovascular exercise has benefits that have been studied and confirmed and that extend far beyond weight management. Sure, use intervals to burn extra calories or take a long run now and again to boost fat consumption, but never classify cardiovascular exercise as "just for losing weight."

This sort of dogma is what makes our clients' lives harder. Be the source of truth and prescribe cardiovascular exercise because it is great for the function of the entire body.

June 16th

Walking on an incline is an underrated but highly effective workout for pushing the endurance capacity of the body without high levels of impact. A significant incline makes a client work much harder than they would on flat ground, thus contributing tremendous cardiovascular benefit. As always, consider the physical condition of the client before prescribing an incline walk.

Think of the last time that you had to walk up a steep hill. Can you remember that burn in your glutes, the soreness you felt in your calves in the days that followed, and just how elevated your heart rate was?

Even if you are in spectacular shape, you have this memory because an incline forces us to work much harder to overcome gravity and move our body forward. Each step might as well be two steps on flat ground.

Your clients can get this benefit too when you design their cardiovascular program. A long Sunday stroll on an incline treadmill or up a local hill can boost their metabolism and enforce your training emphasis on their posterior chain.

June 17th

Ankle mobility is a critical element of running, walking, and even biking. Healthy ankles ensure optimal function of the foot, knee, and hip joints. A client who experiences pain in one of these places may need to improve ankle mobility, specifically dorsiflexion. Once they can adequately move the ankle through space without pain, they can resume their activity.

Often, we get so eager to help our clients achieve their goal of losing weight that we overlook critical details that could, and often do, derail the grand plan.

Ankle mobility is one of those details.

The ability of the ankle to dorsiflex (toe-to-knee) and plantarflex (toe-to-ground) is a critical prerequisite for any running program. It could even have an impact on a simple walking program.

Many clients will require some intervention prior to engaging in their cardiovascular program. Self-myofascial release of the tibialis anterior and gastrocnemius is a great place, as well as traditional dorsiflexion and plantar flexion mobility. You'll always want to invest time in redeveloping your clients' stride mechanics.

June 18th

"Lifting weights faster" is not a replacement for long, sustained cardiovascular exercise. The benefits of cardiovascular exercise extend so much further than simply burning fat and calories. A few sessions of legitimate cardiovascular exercise per week can improve quality of life and the condition and aesthetics of the body. There is no substitute for twenty to thirty minutes of a sustained elevated heart rate at least once a week.

A popular saying amongst strength coaches, bodybuilders, and fitness enthusiasts alike is "skip cardio, just lift weights faster." It may be a funny t-shirt slogan, but it's also inaccurate.

Now, you could lift weights without resting between sets and elicit a cardiovascular response from the body, like what happens in a Tabata class or during a complex circuit.

However, the benefits of cardiovascular exercise extend beyond the metabolic effects most seek. Just one bout of steady state cardio per week can do wonders for a client's entire health profile: brain, body, and spirit.

You are responsible for the total health of your clients and not just their body fat percentage.

June 19th

Cardiovascular exercise should not be a punishment for poor dietary choice. Outside of the fact that it is nearly impossible to burn off a high calorie "cheat meal" in one cardio session, this attitude creates an extremely negative relationship with food and exercise for a client. Exercise should never be used as punishment, period.

There are few things uglier than comparing someone's caloric intake to their need for caloric expenditure. Even worse is developing an exercise program meant to undo someone's intake.

While it may be important to show someone that eating a bucket of ice cream requires a lot of movement to burn it off, instructing them to burn off a certain number of calories to "make good" is unprofessional.

Exercise should be done because it improves the body and pushes us to get better each day. It is not a vessel of punishment for someone who doesn't eat the way you approve of.

It is inexcusable to coach your clients to view calories out as a punishment or justification for calories in. You can do better than that.

June 20th

*While CrossFit has helped many people with strength,
hypertrophy, endurance, fat loss and athletic performance
goals, it highlights one of the risks of cardiovascular
exercise. With exhaustion, quality will begin to go down.
Be sure to respect your client's need for recovery before
attempting a complex lift, a max effort sprint, or any
other movement that could cause injury.*

The phenomenon is real. CrossFit is here to stay, and
many people will continue to utilize it, and similar
workouts, to whip themselves into shape.

As a trainer, you must be wise to its limitations. The high-
risk movements done to exhaustion pose an injury risk to
an underprepared client. This risk might as well double
once you ask that same client to continue performing after
they've become fatigued.

Once movement quality goes down, you must be a
professional and insert a rest period into your client's
workout. Your job is to get them in shape, yes, but
never at the expense of their safety.

Always ask yourself *"at what cost?"* when generating a
challenging circuit.

June 21st

Heart rate variability has been shown to be one of the best indicators of fitness and longevity in the body. Invest some of your personal time into getting to know this complex topic and look to incorporate its factors into your training programs. A healthy heart is a goal that everyone should have.

An advanced form of measurement has come to the forefront of our industry in recent years. While some evidence shows that even ancient Greek physicians used "beat-to-beat" methods to assess health and athleticism, it is only recently that we've learned what to do with those numbers.

The measure of time that passes between beats of the heart (both at rest and during various intensities of exercise) can provide incredible insight into the health of the heart's walls, the function of the sinoatrial node, and even a person's life-span.

You may not be able to assess this accurately at your facility, but knowing about it and understanding it could be beneficial for you as you program exercises for your clients.

June 22nd

*Using cardiovascular exercise as a finisher is perfectly
fine in a personal training session. Just make sure you
apply the appropriate energy system for a client. A client
who regularly does intervals doesn't need more with you.
Just the same, telling a client to do thirty minutes on the
Stairmaster the day after they've done a multi-mile run is
probably redundant. Coach clients toward their needs.*

Consistency is the name of the game in developing
elite-level strength and muscle size. However, cardiovascular exercise requires us to train our bodies in a
way that's different from how we usually train for the
benefits to take hold and elicit change.

Think of the client that you have, you know, the one
who runs ten to twenty miles per week. When they train
with you, you'll want to be emphasizing their strength
training.

That being said, you'll still want to give them some
type of challenge at the end of the workout. This is
where knowledge of the three energy systems and
how we train them is crucial. For this client, you'd
want to train anaerobic intervals since they regularly
train aerobically.

June 23rd

It is common to work with a client who already has a strict running schedule. Many of them will not want to lift weights with their legs. Some will even explain that they "have strong legs" because they run. Do not let this sway you. Training loaded knee-dominant and hip-dominant exercises will strengthen the glutes, hamstrings, quadriceps, and calves, which only boosts running stride power, thus contributing positively to their runs.

In the minds of our running clients, they've done all the training for their legs that they'll ever need. They think that running strengthens their legs and builds quality muscle that keeps them immune from injury or imbalances.

The fact is that running high mileage can consume muscle tissue, lead to muscle and joint imbalances, and even damage one's metabolism if food and strength training aren't present.

So, no matter how much your clients swear they have strong legs, be sure to take the time to build them with loaded movement, focusing on the posterior chain. They will begin to know what truly "strong" legs are.

June 24th

The energy systems—aerobic, glycolytic, and ATP/CP—are always active. Understanding the balance of this spectrum is what separates a great performance coach from a mediocre one. Know when you are working a specific energy system and the impacts it will have on recovery and nutritional needs. What is burned must be replenished.

In life, you eventually come to the realization that everything exists on a spectrum. Political beliefs, people's opinions on music, and how the body recruits muscle fibers or utilizes energy systems all happen along a sliding scale. Few things in life are black and white.

As a coach, you'll discover that your clients are never using only one sort of fuel for any type of exercise. Sure, there is a tendency toward a metabolic pathway based upon exercise intensity, but it is not as if there are three separate funnels for energy.

A great program includes challenges to all three metabolic pathways as well as the appropriate nutrition and regeneration protocol for each. Once a client builds a strong base for each metabolism you can begin to specialize based off their goals.

June 25ᵗʰ

Runners often have issues with the fascial tissue in their feet, calves, quads, and glutes. Utilize self-myofascial release techniques to keep them going pain-free. Be sure to not use these methods on them directly though, as you are not qualified unless you are a physical therapist or licensed massage therapist. Instead, show them how to manage their own myofascial release program.

Any exercise that we engage in is going to cause certain issues to arise in muscles, joints, and fasciae. Repetitive bouts of cardio, especially running, seem to cause the most issues.

This makes it important to increase the frequency of self-myofascial release techniques as your clients increase their running distances or intensity. Attention to the feet, tibialis anterior, calves, hip flexors, tensor fasciae latae, trapezius, pectoralis minor, and glutes is important.

Just remember, unless you are a licensed massage therapist or a physical therapist, you cannot do this work on your clients yourself. You must demonstrate on yourself how to apply the method and remain hands off while they self-myofascial release.

June 26th

There is tremendous value in bodyweight calisthenics. All clients should have a workout for those days that keep them stuck inside their homes. Stringing together five to ten movements that everyone knows can be a tremendous cardio workout for even the fittest person. Simple is effective in this context and can provide enormous value to the long-term effects of exercise programs.

It seems that all the advances in equipment and technology have left calisthenics in the dust.

There are endless possibilities when we begin combining various calisthenic, or bodyweight, exercises into a single workout. A round of push-ups, bodyweight squats, running in place, and doing some jumping jacks can serve as an interval or as part of an aerobic circuit.

There are going to be days that your clients don't want to go to the gym and days that they can't. Providing them with a twenty- to thirty-minute blitz of these exercises keeps them consistent and challenges their cardio.

This is especially valuable to clients who spend a lot of time in hotel rooms.

June 27th

Cardio can increase a person's hunger. The large caloric expenditure will signal the body to seek replenishment, and so a client will actively seek fats and carbohydrates. Take the time to explain that hard cardiovascular exercise is not justification to "eat what you want." It's important to refuel the body with quality nutrients after any intense period of exercise.

Carefully consider the nutritional ramifications of your cardiovascular programming. Everything we ask our clients to do in their workouts is going to influence what they crave in the kitchen.

For example, a ten-mile run is going to trigger hunger, especially for fatty foods, since the body used a lot of stored body fat as fuel. Meanwhile, a challenging series of 1:1 intervals will utilize a lot of ATP and glycogen, making simple carbs a desirable source of nutrition.

Match your dietary prescriptions to the intensity/duration/modality of your exercise program. In doing so you'll enhance performance and better serve the needs of your clients.

It is time the industry stops talking about training and nutrition as if they are widely different topics.

June 28th

Distance running is a bit of an "inverted U" in terms of benefits to the body. A three-mile run is better than a one-mile run, but a nine-mile run might not be better than a five-miler. What this says is: the longer the mileage, the more breakdown can occur in muscles, fascial tissue, and even bones as the body goes catabolic and wear and tear builds up.

Running doesn't always work the way you expect it to.

On one hand, it is a terrific form of exercise that allows the body to move against its own resistance through space while pushing the cardiovascular system to adapt and provide oxygenated blood to the working muscles. It also burns plenty of calories.

On the other, it can do physical and metabolic damage for people who only run. The effects can be worsened by excess distance or frequency. In addition, many people aren't physically ready for the wear and tear that comes from long bouts of running.

Coach your clients to have variety in their training program and avoid the "more is better" mindset.

June 29th

Emphasize getting outdoors whenever possible. A long hike should replace weekend gym homework anytime it can. The benefits of sunlight, fresh air, companionship, and exercise in the outdoors are profound. You may find that clients are more eager to exercise when they don't have to come to the gym.

The benefits of the outdoors cannot be understated in a world where we spend the overwhelming majority of our time indoors.

Whether our clients are at home, at work, at the gym, shopping for groceries, or in their cars, they are not experiencing the benefits of fresh air and sunshine.

Look to find activities for your clients to do outdoors as often as possible. Recommend that they run through their neighborhood instead of getting on a treadmill. Suggest a hike or bike ride with the family on the weekends.

Their bodies and their minds will be better for the

experience. In fact, you may even find that your clients show better adherence to the workouts that take them outdoors.

June 30th

Introduce clients to each other and build a network of people who support one another. Getting three or four clients to commit to meeting each other for Saturday morning cardio without you can build your brand, their loyalty to you, and their body. Create a community of people who are working to make each other better while under your tutelage.

Few things can get us to overcome our internal resistances like an obligation to other people and the bliss that comes from being a part of something bigger than ourselves. We don't want to be "that person" who was late, missed out, or quit.

Build a community with your clients. Introduce them to each other and ask them to help keep each other accountable on the days that they aren't training with you. The group, if set up the right way, will serve as an extension of you and your coaching.

Your clients will stick with each other, push one another, and grow closer to you as their coach. Community makes everything in life a little bit better, so leverage this truth in your business.

July

Business Building

"Freedom is one of the deepest and noblest aspirations of the human spirit."

—*Ronald Reagan*

"A brand for a company is like a reputation for a person. You earn reputation by trying to do hard things well."

—*Jeff Bezos*

July 1st

Present yourself as busy even when you are not. Do not show an empty schedule to new clients if you don't want them to wonder why your schedule is empty. Always create the perception that you are in demand. Suggesting spots for your clients to train instead of asking them when they'd like to come in is a great place to start.

A simple rule in business is to "be in demand." People won't feel compelled to jump for a purchase or invest in a service unless they feel as though they are getting something valuable.

Think of the waitlist for a renowned chef's new restaurant or the price spikes of a hit Broadway show, like Hamilton. Both are examples of something being in demand and people being willing to pay top dollar, or wait an absurd amount of time, for it.

Your business must be in demand as a personal trainer. Never show your clients just how "open" your schedule is. Instead, present yourself as a successful trainer who only has so many spots available for the taking.

Be in demand.

July 2nd

Discounts seem like a great way to attract new clients.
However, they detract from your take-home pay by
making you do the same work for less money per hour.
Instead, add value. Provide a complimentary assessment,
add people into a social media group, or ramp up the
quality of take-home materials you provide to clients.
Don't discount your service if you truly believe you are
worth what you originally charge.

When building your business, or trying to drum up new business, it can be tempting to offer a discount. You are desperate for profits, eager for success, and hoping that anyone will give you a chance.

But, what you've done is hurt your business in the long term. You've told people (accidently) that your service is worth less money. Your discount has set a new price point in their head.

Instead of lowering your price, focus on adding more content, more value, and more experience. Continue adding layers of value that justify your higher price point.

Be memorable because you've given so much, not because you are so cheap.

July 3rd

When meeting a lead, it's best to get the price point of your sessions out of the way first. Just as every car in a dealership has a sticker on its window, you should present your price prior to taking someone through an assessment or session. You want to avoid sticker shock at the end of a session when it's easier to just walk away and say no.

Personal training is a luxury that many people are unable to afford. This is especially true if you are a trainer outside of the bigger cities where median income of your postal code may be lower.

Regardless of what you charge, where you work, or what the income level of your client is, you know that you provide a service that is life-changing.

When having a conversation about your prices, it is best to get it out of the way before you ever train. This way, "the hard part" is over prior to your introductory session/meeting. When you exceed their expectations they'll easily justify your price point.

Avoiding sticker shock is a critical step in getting someone to invest in your programs, and themselves.

July 4th

Avoid closing a session by talking about prices and packages. While it seems logical to discuss these matters at the end, it harms your chances of signing on a new lead or retaining an old one. Always handle business prior to doing what you do best: training. Handle the less attractive matters first and allow the training experience to do the talking.

Pricing is an awkward discussion that can make many people feel "on the spot." The end of a session is a perfect opportunity for your client to see their way out of the conversation. Avoid this situation by addressing all business elements prior to the start of your session.

At worst, you'll avoid that feeling of defeat that comes with having a client walk away from you and say, "Let me think about it." At best, you'll convince them, with your incredible skill and professionalism, that you are worth it.

If you must have the conversation at the end of your session be sure to get them to commit to their next appointment with you prior to discussing price. Drive the attachment to working with you and chances are they'll at least purchase that next session.

July 5th

An email is a simple way of packaging the relevant information a client needs prior to and after a consultation. Prior to meeting for the first time, send them a health form (like a PAR-Q) to streamline the process. After your assessment, send them a thoughtful recap of what they experienced as well as your initial plan going forward. Take the hassle out of the experience and deliver a service that is transparent and efficient.

In a world where our phones receive emails, it's wise to package as much information in an organized message as you can.

Think of that friend you have who has every detail of their vacation planned or outlines all the possibilities for a weekend getaway, complete with bullet points and all. In a sticky situation you know exactly where to look for the information you need.

Be that person in your business by sending your clients comprehensive emails that preview and recap your consultations. This level of professionalism shows that you are willing to work beyond the confines of your training sessions, and in fact, you value efficiency in business.

Sometimes the differentiators in our business exist outside of the scope of exercise science.

July 6th

*Design a program for each person even if they don't
purchase sessions with you. This doesn't mean that they
get access to the program, though. The next time you meet
them, you can go over the program and show them how
prepared you are to get them to their goals. This could be
the effort that sways the sale. If the individual doesn't
purchase, then they'll always remember that you are
a true professional as they embark alone.*

Not all work leads to pay. Obviously, you should be compensated for most of your efforts, but sometimes you'll need to do things without promise of a reward.

Program design is one of those areas. Every person who does a consult with you should have a custom program designed for them that highlights the first four to six weeks of training. They only get the program if they choose to train with you.

At worst, you'll get even more practice designing great programs. At best, your preparation will be exactly what sways them. No matter what, you'll blow them away with your professionalism and preparation. You may even make them jealous as they watch you train someone else with specificity.

July 7th

Set your schedule a month in advance by having your clients commit to their time slots as soon as possible. This allows you to project your workload for the future, adjust people as necessary, and add business when needed. Don't let people's travel, financial issues, or personal problems impact your business. A successful business doesn't happen by accident.

Your schedule is the key cog in your business's wheel. A trainer who doesn't manage their schedule well often struggles with keeping a full book of clients year-round.

Avoid the financial disaster that can occur when all your clients are traveling at once by asking everyone to commit to the coming month's sessions as soon as possible.

Once you have your core clients scheduled, you'll be able to manage the rest of your month more effectively. You can use additional time to take on new clients, work on your own education, or even unwind and take a small trip of your own.

Never let your business run you. Avoid potholes by keeping your eyes forward on the road in front of you.

July 8th

Describe yourself as a coach instead of a trainer. It may sound like semantics, but being a coach elevates you in the minds of all those who consider your services. A trainer is fine and dandy, but a coach is there for the long haul. A coach can have dialogue instead of merely handing out commands.

At first glance, this tip could sound a bit silly, but if you take a moment to understand the definitions of each word, you'll soon see why this subtle adjustment could bring you profits.

A trainer is usually associated with a specific skill or task. People hire trainers to dictate the growth of a skillset. It is a "tell me what to do" sort of job.

A coach is someone who allows information to flow both directions. Think of your favorite coach. It could be a parent, someone from your sporting life, or even a teacher or counselor from school.

They asked questions, listened to your thoughts, and grew with you. They didn't just tell you what to do.

Be a coach for your clients and you will increase retention. People remember "who" you are.

July 9th

*Know your lane in the industry. Do not offer services
for which you are not qualified. Physical therapists,
massage therapists, and strength and conditioning coaches
have worked and studied for long periods of time to
reach where they are. There are legal and ethical
ramifications if you go outside your scope, so be sure to
stick to what you are qualified to do.*

It seems that many personal trainers have built businesses on the pretense that they are the solution to every problem a person may have.

Trainers in gyms across the world have done physical therapy modalities, massage work, and advanced lifting techniques with clients when they weren't qualified or certified.

Don't be one of these fools who puts clients and their own business at risk. Stay in your lane and only conduct business in areas for which you are qualified.

Look to build a network of incredible professionals around you instead of acting as though you are everything to everyone. Your reputation and your business will thank you.

July 10th

*Don't rush finding your niche. Time and experience
will be what help you develop it. You may be passionate
about athletes or postpartum clients when you first start,
but in time, your knowledge and career will send you
in another direction. That is OK and to be expected. Allow
yourself to develop in a variety of directions by keeping
an open mind to all things.*

One of the downsides to the world of social media and marketing is that every fitness professional feels they need to be "the person" for something.

Whether it is a "glute specialist" or a "functional movement guru" or a "body recomposition specialist," it seems people are far too eager to give themselves a title.

Don't rush to these titles and certainly don't limit yourself from exposure to a variety of client types, training modalities, and education tracks. It is by working with the masses that we demonstrate to the world, and to ourselves, what makes us special.

You must excel as a generalist, for a long time, before you can ever become a specialist. Do it all until your work exposes what you do best.

July 11th

It's OK to be a generalist with a few specialties. So many coaches are in a rush to be "the person" for something that they often overlook the core tenants of being a great trainer, coach, and student of exercise. All knowledge is valuable and can be applied to another topic in the field. Develop fully before worrying about standing out.

Yesterday's tip is so important for your growth that we are going to revisit it today.

Your development as a trainer depends most on how wide you've gone with your education and not how deep. The mistake so many young professionals make is finding one thing that they are passionate about and sticking with it until the very end.

If it works, you'll be the best in the business at what you do. However, if something goes awry (and it probably will), then you will lack all ability to reapply your knowledge and jump into other positions in the industry.

Look for opportunities that challenge you to expand beyond your most immediate passions.

July 12th

*Being a professional in the industry means respecting others
around you. Never gossip or downplay the efforts of other
trainers to position yourself above them. Let your work and
customer service speak for itself and let others' mistakes be
their downfall. The best coaches can see the best in others
even when it's hard to find. Be that coach.*

High school behavior is meant to be left behind in the
halls of the school you once walked. It should be kept
in a box next to your cap and gown, your varsity jacket,
and that book of artwork parents always seem to keep.

This is especially true with gossip. No one has ever become
the best in their industry because they spilled the dirt on a
peer. No one has been an upstanding person when they've
spent much of their time diminishing the achievements of
their peers.

Even if someone is doing something worth gossiping
about, stay blissfully uninvolved or offer to help them
correct their course.

Be the coach of the coaches. Be the *person* that other
coaches admire.

July 13th

Always answer emails from leads, clients, and business contacts within twenty-four hours. In fact, try to never close an email without answering it first. Imagine yourself with five minutes before a session and a note from a prospect comes into your inbox. Do you realistically have the time to answer it, or would it be wiser to leave it unread until after your next session? Schedule a time every day for contacting your clients.

Most human beings like to feel important. All human beings loathe the idea of feeling unimportant, especially if they have invested time or money into something or someone.

It's time for you to rewire your business brain and ensure that you answer all contacts within twenty-four hours of them reaching out to you. Doing so ensures that anyone who reaches out to you believes that you care.

Don't have time to answer a longer query? Answer them with an honest email that states, "I'm currently unable to answer this to the level you deserve, so please grant me an extra twenty-four hours to respond fully."

July 14th

When meeting someone on the gym floor in passing,
be sure to say your full name and suggest a time to meet
more formally for a complimentary assessment, a mini-
training session, or just another conversation. You must
be the person to take the initiative.

If you work at a physical location that is a gym and not just a personal training studio, then it is crucial for the members of that gym to know who you are.

Your job is to coach people to and beyond their training goals: a job that is hard to perform if no one knows who you are.

Be sure to introduce yourself to everyone you encounter. Ask them about their training, why they became members of your facility, and if they'd like a sample session or an assessment with you in the near future.

Avoid pushing sales and business during these first interactions, but do recite their first name at least three times and confirm any future meeting in an email within a few hours.

You must be the catalyst for your growing business.

July 15th

Write your biography in a way that speaks more about what you take pride in doing versus all the things you have done. If someone stops to read your bio in the gym, let them be excited to meet the you of today and not the you from yesterday. With that said, don't hesitate to list your accomplishments in a way that makes you stand out.

Writing about yourself in a short-form biography is one of the hardest paragraphs you'll ever write in your life. It just feels weird to reference yourself in the third person and even weirder to describe your vision as a coach.

It can be done, and it must be done. The secret to writing a great biography is spending less of the word count on your accomplishments and credentials and more on your approach as a trainer.

A statement such as, "[Your name] takes clients beyond their goals by designing and implementing a unique and appropriately challenging exercise and lifestyle program for the individual" is a great place to start. It expresses you in the present tense and makes you seem "in the moment."

July 16th

*Business cards are not a necessity, but they don't hurt
either. Keep a batch lying around for events you may
do, passing conversations you'll have in a bar on a Friday, or
for your clients to share with their friends on your
behalf. Oh, and don't put them in your wallet. Get a
business card holder; no one wants a dirty card.*

What an awkward moment it is to meet someone out in public, at an event, or on the floor of your gym and not have a proper way for them to remember your contact information.

A personal trainer needs to have cards on them wherever they go. You could meet your next client in the coffee shop down the street, on the subway, at your local bank, or standing in line at the grocery store.

It should be noted that in our digital culture, the business card can be taken online too. LinkedIn is a great example. It is effectively an online business card that also allows you to list your resume, samples of past work, recommendations, and photos.

You should utilize both mediums, online and print, to ensure that you are getting the maximum amount of exposure for your business.

July 17th

Build your LinkedIn presence to build contacts with other professionals. Develop your Facebook to speak to the network of people you know, groups you are in, and other coaches like yourself. Leave Instagram for speaking to the whole world at once with an image or video. Know the values and risks of each avenue and have a target population in mind for each. A post on one outlet may be a raging success while it goes unnoticed on another.

Social media can be your greatest asset or your biggest weakness, depending on whether or not you play your cards correctly.

Each network provides a different type of audience and that audience should be spoken to in a different way. It is often best to funnel off your social media feeds to only include certain types of content.

Doing so ensures that people who are interested in you are always getting the type of information they'd like to see. Match your content to your audience.

Individuals scrolling through their Instagram feed are less likely to stop for a link to a scientific study whereas your contacts on LinkedIn aren't interested in seeing you doing shirtless pullups.

July 18th

Question yourself before you post to your social media account. Are you going to present yourself as someone who loves showing themselves off or are you providing value to the world around you? This is a question that everyone should ask, especially in a world of shirtless men and half-naked women claiming to be fitness experts. Stand above the crowd by always providing top-notch content with a professional attitude.

Social media is the modern example of the question, "Would you jump off a bridge if your friends did?"

Many fitness professionals simply copy the methods of other successful trainers and fitness personalities and attempt to post similar content. Mirroring is fine in the early stages of your career, but eventually you'll need to cultivate your own voice.

You must ask yourself if you are presenting yourself in a way that you will be proud of after five or ten years of business. Have you laid the bricks of foundation for a dynasty or have you simply thrown together a wooden shack that looks like everyone else's?

July 19ᵗʰ

Wear clothes when posting your photos and videos to social media and blogs. Sure, your legs are incredible, your torso is shredded, and your arms look like they are chiseled from stone. Photos of your body can exist for marketing purposes, but what about a photo of yourself on a random Tuesday? Present yourself as a professional who cares about the clients and not just your muscle definition.

Fitness personalities love to be as naked as possible, it seems. And why not? You've worked hard in the gym building a body you're proud of and you want people to look at you and say, "I want that."

It all makes sense until you realize that empathy is one of the best ways to form real human connection: the type that builds relationships and can make sales.

It may challenge many of the beliefs you currently have, but know that your prospective clients care much more about what you can make *them* look like.

Be modest on your social media channels and instead pour your efforts into showing how much you can help others. Go beyond yourself.

July 20ᵗʰ

When meeting new clients, always probe them for past experiences with trainers, or at the very least, what they expect from a personal trainer. This knowledge allows you to adapt your style enough to meet the client's expectations. Your goal should be to repeat the behaviors that they enjoyed while consciously avoiding those that they didn't like.

Meeting a new personal training client is a lot like dating, much more than many industry professionals would like to admit.

Both people come into the meeting with expectations (that don't always align), wounds from previous experiences, and hopes for a brighter future. With training, it is often the case that your prospect has worked with another fitness professional in the past.

You'll want to do a little digging and find out what made them work with that individual, what they enjoyed, and what they despised. This intel provides you a glimpse at their values, their sensitivities, and what drives their buying decisions.

Knowing more about your prospect is never bad. Listen twice as much as you talk.

July 21st

Develop an elevator pitch of your training style without fancy academic words. Describe your process before results. Everyone in the industry sells results; sell your clients an experience that can't be replicated. Then follow through by delivering results and you'll never be out of work.

It is important to remember that the fancy, scientific words you may use with other coaches are going to go right over the heads of your clients and prospects.

You should be able to describe what you do, and how you go about doing it, to someone you just met in thirty seconds or less. This time frame allows you enough space to:

- Introduce yourself and provide basic credentials (certifications and experience);
- Acknowledge two or three goals that you routinely help people accomplish (e.g. weight loss, muscle gain, or strength);
- Describe your process in a way that someone who hasn't studied exercise science can understand; and
- Present an offer if appropriate.

July 22nd

At the end of every month or training package, reach out to your clients with a feedback survey. Get their pulse on you and your training. Ask them to be honest. You'll demonstrate that you care about their opinion, and if you put their opinion to work, that you listen. At the end of these emails, ask for referrals or for them to spread the word about you on their own social media.

Feedback is the best form of communication between your client and you, especially if it is honest.

Your best bet for eliciting an honest response is to send out an email to each client with a link to an anonymous survey about you. Anonymity will evoke more thoughtful and honest answers.

At the end of the survey, you can ask if they'd be comfortable sharing your profile, or information about you, with their friends. Word of mouth is, and always will be, the most powerful (and most underused) form of marketing.

Regarding the actual feedback from your surveys, be sure to work on the items that your clients suggested that you improve. They don't mean it maliciously. Your clients want to see you grow too.

July 23rd

Gifts for clients are an excellent way to show your support and appreciation. Keep them relatively inexpensive and related to the gym, fitness, or your brand. Don't make a scene when you present it either. Just thank them for their efforts and get back to work.

Being appreciated is one of our basic human needs. All of us feel better about ourselves and life itself when we are noticed, valued, and remembered by those around us.

Your clients are more than customers. They are human beings with lives that begin to intertwine with your own. Remember their birthday, their children's birthdays, and the date you began training.

On these dates, you can give them a little gift, write them a thoughtful note, or put forth an effort to make them feel special. You don't have to spend much money or go too far out of your way either. It is the effort that you put forth that matters most.

You should always celebrate the *person* that you are training. This includes the people, dates, and things in their lives that matter to them.

July 24th

Online training is all the rage now. Which makes sense, considering a single trainer online could help hundreds of people over the course of a month. This is an animal all its own that is significantly harder than anyone expects. Don't think you can make more money and work less by going this route. The best online coaches work all day.

Personal training is a career that allows you the opportunity to directly change people's lives. However, in-person training will always be limited by the number of hours a trainer can, and should, be working. The hours are long and tiring and effectiveness can begin to dip.

Many have turned to online training: an incredible platform that allows you to coach more people than you could ever service in person at a fraction of the time-cost.

It is awesome proof that technology is a net positive for the world. But don't confuse "less time" with "less work." Your integrity online must be equal to that of the sessions that you train in person.

July 25th

Read books on business, finances, and marketing. Just because the authors don't work in fitness doesn't mean they can't provide valuable food for thought. There is plenty you can learn from other industries that will greatly impact your ability to build a successful business. Knowledge is power.

A common mistake many fitness professionals make is reading only what is directly pertinent to the fitness industry. Anatomy, physiology, biomechanics, exercise programming, and beyond are read ad nauseum.

One of the best moves a trainer can make it is to begin studying the thoughts, actions, and processes of successful businesses in other industries.

People don't act differently when they are about to spend their money on fitness. Consumers have behaviors that can be mapped across a variety of industries. Trends in one industry may reappear in another.

This is all valuable information to a personal trainer who wants to earn their best salary.

July 26th

Create a slogan. Something memorable, taggable on social media, and applicable to all populations. #Grindallday sounds great, but it scares away some populations if they aren't comfortable with the idea of "grinding." Use words and phrases that everyone is comfortable with and don't upset anyone.

People like tag lines. It's why every major brand in the U.S. has a jingle, an obvious logo, or a catchy one-liner.

You are no different. Your brand should have a calling card that speaks to you and what you stand for. It should be something that appeals to the people in the front of the line and to those hiding in the back.

Don't feel the need to be cool or trendy and say what you think your customer wants to hear. Be authentic and speak from your heart about what you offer.

Take the time to let it marinate and steadily improve its catchiness until you have crafted your slogan. Be authentic and be memorable. But most importantly, be something that your clients can identify with. After all, they are the ones that will make you go viral.

July 27th

Your business never stops operating. Even when you are off the clock, present yourself in a way that demonstrates your professionalism. Don't play sports like a jerk, don't hog equipment when it's your time to work out, and don't suddenly become a mute in the gym around everyone who doesn't pay you for your time. Any great business expects its employees to represent the brand in a positive light no matter where they are.

When you are your own brand, there is no clock. Even for large corporations like Nike, there is no on-off switch for business mode.

Think of how quickly they cut ties with Tiger Woods after his scandal. They didn't think, "Well, he wasn't wearing a Nike shirt at the time of the incident" and write it off.

Instead, they preserved their brand image by cutting ties with something they couldn't support.

It's important for you to always represent the brand you've created, but it's even more important for you to be the *person* that people have come to trust and invest in. Your reputation is fragile.

Conduct yourself in a way that supports your business, no matter where you are.

July 28th

Building a website is a big step for a personal trainer. It's a chance to announce yourself to the world. Know who you are as a person first and then what you believe in as a trainer. Lastly, ask yourself, "Why would someone choose to listen to me?" If you struggle with these questions, then you don't need a website yet; you need time for reflection until the answers are clearer.

Everything in life has a time and place. While it may sound frustrating to hear, it's exactly what most personal trainers need to embrace.

Far too often, a trainer gets their certification, gains a few paying clients, and begins worrying about their social media profile, designing a website, and building a memorable brand. The cart didn't even wait for the horse to leave the barn.

This mistake is born of eagerness and excitement, not of stupidity. Take a breath and ensure that you know who you are as a person, as a coach, and as a professional before trying to become a branded figure.

Be sure that you can follow through on your promises before yelling to the world that you are the best. Patience is a virtue.

July 29th

Set customer service as a priority in your business. Think about the last time you were wowed by someone's service for you. Don't you want that effect to be felt by everyone you meet? Be the trainer who exceeds everyone's expectations and you can expect to be busy.

Do you remember that waitress who made you feel like you were sitting at the only table in the restaurant? How about the haircut that also included a shave and styling, just because?

Customer relations is the most important part of your business in the service industry. You are very literally working with the client who is paying you. There are no middle-men, no shipping routes, and no corporate policies to hide behind when you are face-to-face with your end customer.

You don't have to assume the customer is always right either. That's horrible advice. You *do* have to treat your customer well and help them find the right solution.

Your goal should be to "WOW" someone as often as possible. Create memories, big and small, whenever you are given the chance.

July 30th

Think about your network. Do you know people in other industries? Do you know people who could work alongside you to help a client reach their goals more effectively? Doctors, nutritionists, physical therapists, psychologists, food services, and even your favorite laundromats could be the right connection for your client.

The most successful person in any industry isn't usually the smartest, the most gifted, or even the hardest working.

It's usually the person who has built a reliable network of people who can step up to the plate to handle matters that they themselves can't, or shouldn't, be dealing with.

As a trainer, your network should include primary care physicians, nutritionists, physical therapists, other coaches, and even dentists, laundromats, and child-care services.

The master connector can solve multiple problems for their customer with nothing more than a phone call. This sort of system makes you indispensable to everyone in your network.

July 31st

Your business reflects you. If you are not put together, or if you have a habit of running late, or if you don't always follow through, your business will share these properties. Don't rush things if you still must work on youself. A complete person runs a better business and a better business makes more money.

The mirror is where your business lies. The image you see staring back at you is what your customers see. What does everyone see?

Take the time to address your shortcomings and your business will improve. Face any demons you've kept locked in your basement, challenge yourself to get more sleep, to stop worrying about what others think, and to rise above the noise that holds so many back.

You can get to the exact place in your business that you are dreaming of if you take the time to clean yourself up and bring a better version of yourself to work every day.

The machine is only as good as its parts, but both are only as good as their maintenance.

August

Nutrition

"August brings into sharp focus and a furious boil everything I've been listening to in the late spring and summer."

—Henry Rollins

"Our bodies are our gardens and our wills are our gardeners."

—William Shakespeare

Day by Day

August 1st

Like exercise, there is no perfect diet. Each person brings a unique anatomy and genetic build, and understanding this is critical to writing someone a nutrition plan. Nutrition is not a blanket that can cover all people the same way. You must account for daily habits, predispositions, allergies, and likes/dislikes when trying to guide someone.

Our unique traits are what make the world interesting. If we were alike, then life would be boring and devoid of flair.

Instead, our differences are aplenty and on display, which means that there is no one-size-fits-all approach in health and fitness.

While it may be tempting to tell every client to follow a specific diet, eat specific foods, or do specific forms of exercise, you must account for the subtle variations between us all.

Many factors come into play when creating a person's nutrition program: their schedule, their allergies, their aversion to certain foods, and their budget, just to name a few.

Your nutrition prescriptions should be just as unique as the individuals who you are prescribing them to.

August 2nd

Eating is just as much psychological as it is physiological. Consider this: how many people love dieting? The answer is few, if any. Denying ourselves the simple pleasures in life, such as a sweet treat, can cause psychological pain and deprive us from "feel-good" hormones such as dopamine and serotonin, which is why many clients can't seem to say no to a cheat meal.

Many wise people have discussed the importance of not giving into your desires on a regular basis. The Stoics, Greek philosophers, and modern billionaires have all been quoted on the discipline to overcome pleasure.

We must remember that our clients, like ourselves, are imperfect humans who feel temptation and shame. They know that they shouldn't be eating a box of cookies at night, but they do it anyway.

It's because the "feel-good" hormones are far more powerful than the pride they feel when they say no. It's completely human.

Coach your clients to be disciplined and challenge them to say no to many of their cravings. Yet, do so because you understand the power of human emotions and not because you choose to ignore them.

August 3rd

Ask your clients about their previous experiences with dieting, nutrition, and calorie-counting. Most people have tried it at some point in their lives, if not multiple times, and will have plenty of feedback for you. This is crucial information.

It is highly likely that every person you ever encounter has at least contemplated dieting at some point in their lives. Most have tried.

These experiences, for better or for worse, are a part of the client you are training. It's important to ask questions and learn about a person's past experiences with nutrition and dieting prior to making any of your own recommendations.

The information you gain will help you create processes and habits that are achievable by your clients instead of making another blanket recommendation that lasts a few weeks before ultimately being discarded.

A person's motivation is often the product of previous experiences. Tap into those memories and lessons and you'll be better able to guide your clients toward their goals.

August 4th

Sleep is one of those factors that is talked about constantly, but few people truly understand its importance for nutrition. Insufficient amounts of sleep lead to poor decisions when it comes to food, an increased need for simple carbohydrates, and a lack of desire to train effectively. If you are coaching nutrition with your clients, then you'd be wise to begin talking about their sleeping habits.

It doesn't matter how great an exercise program is or how specific a dietary plan becomes if a person isn't getting enough rest.

Sleep is the human body's primary mode for recovery: a necessary act to heal from the mental, physical, and emotional stress of the day.

Your clients are probably sleep-deprived, as are you, and it's holding everyone back. Begin by coaching at least six to seven hours of sleep. Slowly progress toward recommendations of eight or nine hours when possible and maintaining a similar sleep/wake schedule on the weekends.

Sleep is that important. It can't be compromised, at least not for long, if our clients are to achieve their fitness goals.

August 5th

It's easy to suggest eating more protein for those looking to build muscle and gain weight, but learning what is a healthy amount of protein for people who aren't training like athletes or bodybuilders is crucial. Half of someone's bodyweight (in pounds) in grams is an excellent and safe place to start. Adjustments can always be made.

Over the last decade, the answer to "What should I eat?" has almost unanimously become "More protein." This macronutrient has been framed at as the perfect calorie.

It does fuel muscle growth, it does keep you full, and it can help decrease body fat over time. Protein is necessary for life and for fitness.

But it isn't the "miracle drug" that so many claim it to be. It is a macronutrient, one of three, and it must be consumed in appropriate amounts depending upon a person's metabolism and body composition.

Each person you train will need a different level of protein consumption. A semi-active person needs much less than an athlete and a sedentary person even less.

August 6th

The backbone of anyone's diet should be vegetables. A common recommendation is at least seven to ten servings a day. Most clients will balk at so many vegetables, but with your coaching, they'll eventually learn that it is attainable. Start by adding a serving or two per week until the goal is achievable.

What is grown in the ground is undoubtedly the best for our bodies. For thousands of years, we have relied on the plants that grow from the soil and the fruits that are born from trees to feed our bodies.

While proteins and fats are critical elements of a diet, our commitment to vegetables is what allows us to maintain an optimal body mass while living a long and healthy life.

Emphasizing seven to ten servings of vegetables per day is going to simplify many clients' attempts to cut calories and lose weight.

A diet with so many vegetables will usually be lower in calories and higher in valuable nutrients, which is key for sustainable weight loss. This is especially true when consuming vegetables high in fiber, a nutrient that contributes to fullness.

August 7th

The reason vegetables are so important to our diets is that they are high in insoluble fiber, low in calories, and full of micronutrients, aka vitamins and minerals. Building a diet around vegetables ensures you get the proper amounts of naturally occurring vitamins and minerals while staying full on low-calorie, low-glycemic foods.

Continuing yesterday's conversation about vegetables, we will take an extended look at why vegetables are so important.

Vegetables provide high nutrient density (fiber, vitamins, and minerals) while having low caloric density: a perfect food for filling stomachs while avoiding the over-consumption of calories.

A diet that gets enough vitamins and minerals is one that better supports the body. These nutrients are critical catalysts necessary for a thriving metabolism and a healthy immune system.

The high fiber and water content also keeps the body more satiated, which is a key element of dietary satisfaction. No one likes to feel hungry. In fact, many people find that they snack significantly less when they consume enough vegetables.

August 8th

Providing a standard "weight loss" diet to a client doesn't factor in many things such as allergies, sensitivities, and health issues. It's important to outsource to a registered dietician who is capable of handling specific issues that require a more refined approach when necessary.

Unfortunately, weight loss can be even harder for some people than for others. The presence of allergies, sensitivities, G.I. dysfunction, hormone dysfunctions, and immune diseases can make the standard "weight loss" diet completely ineffective or dangerous.

It is important to recognize when a person's needs exceed your capabilities. You must refer out to a registered dietician as soon as your client mentions a medical condition. This is both a legal and an ethical point and one that can never be argued with.

Work side-by-side with an RD when these instances occur so that you have a better understanding of everything that is happening.

Don't worry about losing your client either. In fact, you'll build more trust with your client by ensuring that they get the best information/service possible. They'll reward you with loyalty.

August 9th

Fruits are another great source of vitamins and minerals even if they are of higher calorie and higher glycemic value than their vegetable buddies. Two servings for most people is plenty, although athletes and those looking to gain muscle could benefit from as many as four servings of fruit per day.

Fruits are the tastier cousins of vegetables: a sweet treat full of vitamins and minerals.

Unlike vegetables though, fruits have a cap on them regarding servings per day. They contain similar vitamins and minerals to vegetables but have higher levels of sugar.

While eating a few servings of fruit is certainly better than candies and sodas, it's important to help clients understand that too much sugar, from any source, can cause G.I. disruption and insulin sensitivity issues.

Most people should keep to two or three servings of fruit each day. It is best if these servings consist of a variety of different fruit types (berries, citrus fruits, and pome fruits). This will diversify the vitamin and mineral content and provide maximum benefit.

August 10th

Understand the variety of diets. Vegan, kosher, halal, pescatarian, keto, and so many others are often misunderstood. It's important to know the difference between them and avoid making blanket statements that could damage your credibility or offend your clients' beliefs. Being informed is always a good idea.

People embrace a variety of diets for a variety of reasons and it is important for every fitness professional to respect their clients' choices and not attempt to force a new way of life.

For some it's religion, for others it may be animal rights, others have allergies, and some just go with the crowd. The best coaches ask questions like, "Why does this diet work for you?"

Your job when someone sticks to a method or belief system is to coach them to the best of your ability within their limitations. Adjust your prescriptions to include and respect their choices/rules.

Coach without judgment and with the intention to make your client the best they can be while respecting their choices and needs.

August 11th

Every food you consume has cells that are not of your body.
You are a human and food is, well, not human. Thus, every
time you eat, your gut is breaking down foods into useable
molecules that make sense to your body. This is a stress that
should be accounted for with scheduled fasts that allow time
for the body to digest and heal. It is often beneficial to stop
eating a few hours before bed or delay breakfast for an hour
two after waking to give the body time to heal.

Fasting has become a hot topic within the fitness industry and for good reason. There is a lot of literature that supports intermittent fasting for weight loss. We aren't examining fasting for this purpose though.

Instead, it is about looking at the myriad of health benefits that a temporary fast can provide. By allowing the immune system a chance to rest you empower it to do its job that much better when it is revved up.

We must remember that we actively break down cells that are not human when we consume food. This workload can tire out the body. The occasional, or regular, fast can do wonders for resetting these mechanisms.

August 12th

Allergies are the severe end of food sensitivities. However, we all possess or lack traits that make us incapable of properly digesting a food type. Take note of the patterns that form over time when you, or a client, eat certain foods. Take these items out of a diet and see if the symptoms subside. After a while, reintroduce the food and see if symptoms return. This will zero in on if a sensitivity exists.

One of the most unfortunate events in nutrition is the presence of a sensitivity to a food that is seemingly safe, or worse, delicious.

Many people walk around with sensitivities to nuts, grains, dairy, specific legumes, seeds, and even some types of vegetables. It all comes down to the body releasing histamines as a reaction to the foods: an inflammatory response that can wreak havoc on the immune system and contribute to other issues.

If a client reports not feeling well after eating certain foods, then look to cut those foods out of their diet for a while, even if they are healthy. Through elimination, you'll be able to heal the gut and retest the food in the few weeks to confirm a sensitivity.

August 13th

Simple carbohydrates can be loaded into a person's diet around intense workouts to boost performance but minimize the potential downsides of the calories. Even an individual who is dieting can enjoy a potato, grains, or fruits around the time that they exercise. Be sure to dose the carbohydrates appropriately to the person's bodyweight and caloric needs though.

Athletes of a variety of disciplines have utilized carbohydrate loading to perform better in competition for many years.

By properly loading glucose and glycogen into the muscles, liver, and blood, a person can have a much greater store of energy available during exercise. These stores are what drive the glycolytic energy system.

This strategy is great for clients who may be attempting a personal best during a session or competing in a specific event while with you. The preloading of fuel increases output and improves recovery between bouts of effort.

You can utilize this strategy with clients who are trying to lose weight too, so long as you manage the timing and dose of the carbohydrates. The quality of carbohydrate matters too.

August 14th

Fats are a critical element of the human diet. Without enough dietary fat, cells lose their structure over time and the body begins protecting its own stores for survival purposes. Be sure to coach your clients to eat diets that are rich in mono and poly unsaturated fats. Believe it or not, a diet with the right amount of fats in it might just be the secret to a healthier, leaner body. Sources such as fish, nuts, and seeds are best.

If you were to build a time machine and go back to the 1990s, you'd see an absolute hysteria over the fat contents of food. This is where the entire low-fat craze began. Suddenly, fats were taken out of foods and replaced with sugars, salts, and chemicals.

This was a huge mistake, as plenty of scientific research has shown that fats aren't the primary contributor to increasing body fat. In fact, a diet lacking in dietary fat can limit someone's ability to use their own bodyfat as fuel. Think of it as a protection mechanism the body has to prevent someone from starving.

Ensure that your clients are eating enough fats in their diet, especially if they are trying to lose weight. The unsaturated fats that come from nuts, seeds, oils, and fish will be best for them.

August 15th

*Saturated fats get a negative reputation for their
propensity to clog arteries and contribute to weight gain.
However, it is important to distinguish between saturated
fats that come from potato chips and baked goods versus
that which is found in red meat and oils. Coach your clients
to consume their saturated fat, in appropriate amounts,
from non-processed foods.*

Saturated fats aren't the best calorie in the world for living a healthy lifestyle due to their potential to cause damage to the cardiovascular system (via increased LDL, increased inflammation of the body, and potential fat accumulation around the vital organs), but they shouldn't be avoided altogether.

Foods with saturated fats are necessary for hormone production, fat metabolism, and are often full of vitamins and minerals.

The key when eating saturated fats is to choose natural sources over baked goods and other snack foods. Meats, oils, and even grass-fed dairy can improve one's health if their serving size is controlled. So too can coconuts and avocados.

August 16ᵗʰ

Every other week there's a new fad in the realm of nutrition. Your clients will likely hear them before you do, and that is completely normal. When these topics are brought up during your training sessions, avoid the urge to have an emotional response. Ask for time to do research and provide them with a thoughtful and respectful answer in your next session.

At the core, all diets are the same: reduce caloric intake from sources that are high in carbohydrates, salts, and chemicals. Some ask you to slash carbohydrates while others have you avoid anything that wasn't available five-thousand years ago.

Our clients are often going to hear of these new diets and feel that urge to follow them as if they had finally found the answer to their most burning question. While most diets are complete hogwash, it's important to do your due diligence and inform yourself about them.

You may still turn your clients away from the diet, but you'll do so with an earnest recommendation and respect. This type of conversation leads to better success in the long term.

August 17ᵗʰ

Nutrition is a tough place to get complete honesty from your clients. Build an environment that is OK with less-than-perfect. Don't yell or get upset with a client who had a rough weekend and don't celebrate choosing kale. You are the coach and not a judge. Leave the emotions to them.

For many clients, it's easier to lie to their trainer than to face their wrath for having a cheat meal (or weekend).

They'll tell you they ate their vegetables, avoided the extra drink, and even worked out on the weekend.

Except they didn't.

Create an environment for your clients to feel safe in. Allow them to be honest even when they falter. This honesty allows for you to better coach them to avoid pitfalls and achieve results.

It's the classic example of "people don't care how much you know until they know how much you care." Show your clients you care about them by honoring the human side of personal training.

If your clients can't trust you, the coach they've hired to guide them, then who can they trust?

August 18th

The most important element of nutrition coaching may be the need to create a healthy relationship with foods for your client. Foods aren't good or bad. They are just information being put into your body and not the reflection of good and evil. Some information is better than others of course, but it is important to help your clients avoid guilt at all costs.

If you are going to coach nutrition with your clients, then it is imperative for you to understand that there are no "good" or "bad" foods.

Surely some information is better than other information. In fact, consistently taking in good data is much better than taking in bad data. Still, we must not assign a value of virtue to calories.

Avoid allowing clients to develop a negative relationship with food and exercise. We don't want them rationalizing food with exercise or exercising harder because of certain foods.

We want them to eat foods with a desire to improve their body's function and exercise because they want to improve their capacity. We want them to eat because it does their body good, not because they want to make good.

August 19th

Weight loss is the most common reason someone begins a nutrition plan, but it is not the only reason someone may need one. It is important to round out your knowledge to include weight gain, athletic performance, and lowering specific biomarkers such as cholesterol and blood pressure.

When most people hear the word "diet," they picture someone trying to lose weight. That's mostly true, but many people go on diets for other reasons.

For example, a college freshman athlete may go on a higher calorie diet to increase his body mass to compete.

An elite runner may go on a high carbohydrate diet while preparing for a long race.

Others may hire a registered dietician to help them lower their cholesterol, decrease their blood pressure, or even heal their digestive system from a lifetime of inflammation.

As a coach, you must know that there are a variety of reasons someone would go on a diet and be prepared to work with someone who has goals that are very different from the usual.

August 20ᵗʰ

*No matter the motivation, it's important to keep a client
focused on behaviors that they can control instead of on
the outcome that they desire. Wanting to lose ten pounds
isn't why someone loses ten pounds. It's the accumulation
of actions and non-actions that creates the weight loss.
Skipping the cake and choosing to be in bed for a full eight
hours of sleep is the action that matters.*

Think about the last time in your life that you really
wanted something. You thought about it as soon you
woke up and every time you went to bed.

That's how many of your clients feel about their weight
loss goals. So, as you coach them, it's important to honor
their desires and respect their urgency. Show your clients
that you understand that their success is important.

The most helpful thing you can do is to keep their focus
on their daily behaviors: sleeping, eating vegetables, and
staying in motion. It is the sum of these actions that will
get results and not merely thinking about the goal.

They'll want to stray. They'll quote the scale every time
they see you. But refocus them back on the actions that
lead to success and soon enough they'll see the results
they so desperately crave.

August 21st

Habits should have the most emphasis in nutrition coaching. Instead of prescribing a specific diet, it is better to propose cornerstone habits, such as water intake or servings of vegetables per day, that when done consistently create an environment for nutritional success. Habits are easier to manage and allow for people to develop autonomy with their own nutrition—a goal every coach should have.

We are the product of what we do most. If you read every day, then you could be quite intellectual and cultured. If you exercise every day, then you might be fit.

It's important to remind our clients of this truth in life. They exercise when they feel like it and eat nutritious foods when it's convenient. The healthy lifestyle is not habitual for them.

Focus your coaching on establishing these healthy habits, one at a time if you must, to ensure your clients can lose fat, build muscle, and achieve their ideal body.

More importantly, this helps them keep it for the rest of time. Create the results while providing the tools to keep them. That is your real value.

August 22nd

A caloric deficit is needed for someone to lose weight.
However, there is a limit to how large that deficit should
be. Ensure your clients aren't avoiding food or cutting
calories too low in their effort to see results. Too much of a gap
and the body will protect body fat stores and begin shutting
down. Don't slash calories blindly and expect
good results. Everything should be calculated.

Did you know that the 2000 calorie per day diet is factually unsupported?

Research and aggregated data showed that a national average would be closer to 2,350 calories per day, but an FDA poll showed scientists felt it was discouraging and might cause overeating if the recommendation were at the actual average, so they rounded down (found in Marion Nestle's *Food Politics*).

All of this is to say that blindly cutting someone's caloric intake by 500 or 1000 or to achieve a certain total such as 1500 or 2200 is just as irresponsible.

There are formulas readily available on the internet and within the textbooks of elite certifications such as Precision Nutrition. You have no excuses to wing it.

August 23rd

There is no ideal number of meals per day. Some people like five or six small meals while others prefer a traditional big three. Some intermittent fasters only have one large meal and a few snacks. The point here is that success can be had at any meal count. The important factor is finding which plan your client can adhere to.

How many meals a person should consume per day became a hotly debated topic after a few scientific papers showed evidence of increased metabolic efficiency when eating smaller meals more frequently.

It's important to remember that the number one factor in people's ability to gain, lose, or maintain a bodyweight will always be caloric intake. If someone is eating the right amount of food for their body and their goals, then they'll be OK.

How we get those calories tends to be more customizable. Some people thrive on higher frequency and lower calorie density while others do just the opposite. The key is to discover what works for your client and stick to it.

August 24th

If your client has been successful in integrating three or four new habits into their lives and has seen positive change in their body, then they might be ready for a more specific diet. When it is time to prescribe a diet, it's important to start with the "problem" meal first, that is, the meal during your client's day that seems to go awry more often than it goes well.

Many clients believe that all they need to succeed is a diet that tells them what to eat and when to eat it, and someone to make sure they listen.

If this were true, we would have slapped the obesity epidemic in the face and wouldn't be where we are now. Information is everywhere and there is no shortage of trainers pushing people to eat healthier foods.

Clients must build healthy habits before ever focusing on a specific diet, such as keto or carbohydrate cycling. While they create results, they must be done by people who have already mastered the tenants of healthy living prior to beginning.

You must learn to ride a bike before getting onto a motorcycle. Your clients must learn how to habitually do right by their body before embarking on any challenging, or specific, dietary regimens.

August 25th

*There is an issue with portions, especially in developed
countries where food is available in excess. Have a sit-down
conversation with your nutrition clients and discuss the
serving size of various foods to ensure that they are seeing
their meals through the correct lens. Most people greatly
overestimate what an appropriate serving size is, which
might just be their primary downfall.*

The portion size of a typical meal has gotten out of
control in developed countries like the U.S.

Go to any chain restaurant and order a lunch or dinner
and you'll find thousands of calories delivered to you,
hot and ready.

Many clients have begun to label this sort of gluttony
as being a normal meal. They won't feel full until they
feel uncomfortable: more is better. And this is a major
problem.

Demonstrate what real serving sizes are to your clients.
Recalibrate their expectations of a meal and explain to
them that their body isn't supposed to handle that much
food at once. Help them get back to normal.

August 26th

Learn which vegetables, nuts, and beans provide high levels of protein per serving. It is easy to tell your clients to eat baked chicken or fish until they hit their numbers, but the truth is that many people don't enjoy eating that much meat or fish. Recommending servings of sprouts, lentils, and black beans can help your clients achieve their goals, diversify their diet, and ease the burden of meeting protein goals.

Protein consumption is a critical habit for someone to master if they'd like to achieve their ideal weight, exercise optimally, and live a healthy life.

Thankfully, most coaches recommend that their clients eat at least half of their bodyweight in grams of protein.

Many trainers focus on meats, poultry, fish, dairy, and supplements when talking about great sources of protein. While this isn't wrong, it's important for a coach to expand their knowledge of plant-based proteins, such as vegetables, legumes, nuts, and seeds. This diversity in sourcing can give a client more options to hit their protein targets.

August 27ᵗʰ

Nutrition advice is around every corner. It seems that anyone who has ever exercised or read an internet article has an opinion. Realize that in many conversations you'll have the least popular opinion but the most effective solution. Your clients may be your worst enemy at times as they compare you to their friend at the office or an article that they saw on social media. Hold your ground and coach the principles of true nutrition.

The deeper you dive into nutrition and the more you learn about the digestive tract, the endocrine system, the metabolic pathways, and the mechanisms of weight management, the more your clients will doubt you.

You could have a PhD in dietetics and still be doubted by a room of average-minded individuals if you state an unpopular truth or go against what they believe. It's called cognitive bias: no one wants to believe that they are wrong.

Understand this: you know the way. If you've done your homework studying the finer parts of the human metabolism, then you are the expert on the matter. Your challenge becomes learning how to share what you know in a package that is well-received.

August 28th

Clients will stray from nutrition plans and that is OK.
Have your clients understand that perfection is not the goal,
progress is. Provide them tips for navigating restaurants and
social evenings, but don't hound them to bring their own
meal to a restaurant or avoid all cocktails at an event they
are looking forward to. Coach the person and not perfection.

Sometimes your clients just won't adhere to their diet. They'll knowingly and blissfully jump off the boat and into waters they once swore off.

You must be OK with this and accept them for what they are: humans. Like you, sometimes they just don't want to try. Sometimes they want to throw their hands up and say, "Screw it."

While you shouldn't encourage this behavior or let it go unnoticed, a coach understands that they are a guide and not a dictator.

Ask questions about why they chose to do what they did. Come to understand the emotions that drove the actions instead of simply zeroing in on the actions and demonizing them for slipping up.

August 29th

*When clients travel, they are often thrown way out of sync.
Their sleep, diet, and daily flow are disrupted, whether it
is business or pleasure. Sit down with them prior to a trip
and help map out the healthier restaurants near their hotel,
prepare snacks, and plan for the unexpected. While not
every pitfall can be avoided, careful planning can keep
the trip from spiraling out of control.*

Coaching doesn't end when a client walks away from
you. In fact, many would argue that your coaching is
just beginning when your client leaves the gym.

Many of your clients will have travel, whether for work
or pleasure, and they'll need help planning. Help them
study their destination. Find a gym they can exercise in,
local restaurants that can honor their dietary requests,
and teach them how to make tasty but healthy snacks
for traveling.

The best results come from consistency, which doesn't
end just because someone is traveling. Create a pathway
to success for your clients while they are away from you
and they'll be more likely to achieve their goals.

August 30ᵗʰ

Realize that nutrition advice is nothing more than advice. Unlike a training session in which you literally direct your client to do something in the moment, a nutrition session provides advice that they must follow when you are not around. Coach with the intent for them to listen and succeed but understand that some people struggle to get out of their own way.

The thing about nutrition is this:

You can only do so much for your clients. You can teach them all about the macronutrients, write specific diets, take them shopping for groceries, and help them develop habits for success.

But they're still the ones putting food in their mouths. They will spend significantly more time away from you than they will with you, and many times they will make decisions that you wouldn't have made for them.

You must be OK with the fact that nutrition coaching is simply advice and that you can do your absolute best and the person will still struggle to succeed and remain consistent.

August 31st

Simple is always best. There is enough diet and exercise information available to fill tome after tome. Don't fill your clients' heads with the details of ketosis if they don't need it or prescribe advanced carbohydrate cycling if they can't even eat a normal day's worth of vegetables.

Whether it is out of a true desire to give a client the best value for their money or a way of flexing their intellectual ego, many coaches over-program nutrition with their clients.

Most people walking around want moderate results in exchange for moderate effort. They don't want to suffer through ketosis and they don't want to count every calorie they put in their body.

They don't have to either. So, focus your nutrition practice on the simple basics: vegetables, proteins, water intake, avoiding processed foods, and getting enough sleep.

You'll be surprised by just how effective simple can be. Try it with your next client. Start with the simplest of recommendations and let them work at nailing those behaviors down.

September

Coaching Cues and Tactics

"In many ways, September feels like the busiest time of the year: The kids go back to school, work piles up after the summer's dog days, and Thanksgiving is suddenly upon us."

—Brene Brown

"Each person holds so much power within themselves that needs to be let out. Sometimes they just need a little nudge, a little direction, a little support, a little coaching, and the greatest things can happen."

—Pete Carroll

September 1st

A great coach doesn't count every repetition out loud or provide positive reinforcement each time. Instead, they watch quietly and provide coaching cues as they are needed. Talking less is more effective than providing constant noise.

Coaching is often about what you don't say instead of what you do say. The best coaches in any field know what to say and when to say it and leave it at that.

This methodology flies in the face of what every rookie trainer feels they should be doing when engaging in a training session. From counting each repetition out loud, complimenting each effort, or trying to give detailed coaching while the client is moving, there is just too much noise.

Learn to pick and choose your spots. Count only the repetitions near the end of a set, save encouragement for the times when a client really excels, and only coach when a client is available to listen.

It takes practice, but over time you'll find yourself talking less and saying more.

September 2nd

Repetition counts should be discussed as a range prior to the beginning of a set. Set an expectation (with wiggle room) that allows your client to know their goal prior to starting. Only verbally acknowledge repetitions once you enter the range you prescribed.

Clients should know what is expected of them prior to a training set. This includes how to do the exercise well and just how much effort is expected of them.

Giving a specific repetition count isn't your best coaching tactic though. Instead, laying out a range of repetitions (say eight to twelve) provides your client a chance to push a set further or for you to reign it back if their form breaks down early.

This freedom keeps a client from feeling as though they underperformed. If you choose a weight that a client should be able to perform for ten repetitions, then a range of eight to twelve provides space for optimal and suboptimal performances.

A successful coach prepares for the best days and the worst equally. Sometimes your clients just won't have it and other times they'll blow you away with their performance.

Day by Day

September 3rd

Provide detailed coaching and feedback just before the next set of an exercise. Allow your client to work (unless a critical flaw is presenting itself) and then bring their heart rate down with a little rest before coaching them further. It is very hard to work and listen at the same time, so we want to avoid bogging down our clients with too much at once.

The human brain is quite amazing, but it can still get bogged down by too much input at once, especially if input and output are occurring simultaneously.

This is exactly what happens when you are trying to give your client detailed coaching mid-repetition. Their brain is dedicating a large amount of energy and power to their efforts plus you are talking at them, and they feel obligated to listen.

This causes a sort of paralysis in the body, where a person is either listening too much to move or moving too much to listen. When this happens, both parties involved can get frustrated.

Avoid this by coaching between sets. Save your explanations for the moments where your clients can listen to you.

September 4th

Once an exercise begins, coaching cues should be no more than three-word remarks. "Chest up" or "drive the floor" are great cues that don't bog down your client's mind by providing them too much data to process while working through a physical task. Let them work unless they might get hurt.

You can, and should, continue to coach while a client is in motion. Your cues, however, should become much simpler, shorter versions of something you've already discussed.

"Chest up" is a great example of this. Prior to a set of squats, you may say to a client that they must create more thoracic extension and stay tall and tight underneath the barbell. Once the next set begins, you'll want to avoid this mouthful of jargon by simply saying, "chest up" when your client begins to lose position.

This sort of coaching is most effective when the client is in action. It's short, sweet, and drives home a specific point. Keep everything simple once your client begins their exercise and you'll see a tremendous increase in their ability to adapt.

September 5th

Coaching cues that are internal in nature focus on something that is going on, or should be going on, inside of the body. Cues such as "flex your glutes," or "pinch your shoulder blades together" are effective but require the client to understand both function and anatomy. While these cues may seem helpful, many clients don't know how to do the actions you ask, so it may better to emphasize more easily understandable external cues.

Knowing the difference between your internal and external cues is critical for a trainer to be successful in communicating with their clients.

Many clients have no idea where their biceps are or how to squeeze their glutes. These are individuals for whom internal cues would only lead to further confusion.

However, they may respond to something like "flex your Arnold muscles" or "hold a credit card in your backside." These relatable actions or images make sense to them.

Know when to use what type of cue and with which populations your cues work best. Your goal is to communicate effectively.

September 6th

Coaching cues that are external in nature are the best because they emphasize an action that is done into the world. "Push the floor away" and "bend the bar" are two image cues that invoke common actions. Typically, these are the best cues for getting a client to succeed since the images are understandable and require no prior knowledge to execute.

Our brains are wired to make associations. If someone says the word "apple," you may have a variety of connected thoughts pop into your head:

"Computers," "phones," "red," "fruit," "oranges," or "Johnny," just to name a few. These snap responses are because our brain stores information in categories.

This phenomenon works to your advantage as a personal trainer if you can help your clients build associations between what you want them to do and something unrelated to fitness that they can picture.

"Max your tension on the bar" is a great cue, but it is said better as "bend the bar."

The same goes for "push the floor away" instead of "jump as high as you can."

September 7th

Some of the best cues have a personal touch or memorable quip involved. "Crack diamonds with your glutes" by Dean Somerset stands out, as does "Make like Superman," a cue to lengthen the spine used by Nick Winkleman, formerly of EXOS, with a client whose son loved Superman. Be memorable if you'd like your clients to remember what you say.

Some of the best cues for us make absolutely no sense to those around us. It only matters if our clients understand them.

Once during a seminar, Nick Winkleman detailed a story where he couldn't get his client to get tall and reach full length. Over time, he learned that his client's son loved Superman, and it clicked. He told his client, "Get long and strong like Superman," and change happened.

It can be this simple. You can make cues funny or specific based on the information your clients give you about their lives and experiences. Coaching people to emulate actions they take in their daily lives or used to do in sport is another specific example of client-centered cuing practices.

September 8th

Realize that most clients are not interested in a secondhand kinesiology degree. While the deep science may be exciting to you, and even seem relevant, you'll want to keep your teaching simple enough that a fifth grader could understand it. Avoid slowing down the pace of a session in favor of diving into the nitty-gritty of anything that has technical terms in it. Keep a shorthand version ready for moments like this, but don't waste time becoming a gym floor professor.

Think of all the times you've learned something interesting and wanted to run and tell everyone about it. You were eager to teach.

That sort of passion should never be suppressed, but be wise when you engage your clients about the science that drives your practice.

They aren't interested in your weekend explorations of the Krebs cycle and VO_2 max training. Some will care, but most will not.

Keep your teachings simple and your methods effective. Teach only what can truly stick in your clients' minds and leave the rest out.

September 9th

Some science does need to be discussed with clients, such as the difference in muscle fiber types and why we train heavy and light, and you'll need to be prepared. Take time to prepare your elevator pitches for some major exercise concepts. If you can deliver a simple and effective message in fifteen seconds, then you'll have succeeded. Schedule time with a client to meet outside of a session if they care to know more.

Just because you don't want to be the gym floor professor doesn't mean you can't be prepared with great Cliff Notes on the prominent subjects of the field.

As you continue to educate yourself, take the time to rewrite what you've learned in your own words. Look to explain complex topics in simple language.

It is this language that you'll use to communicate to your clients when they ask questions about your programs and methods. You'll be able to teach them why you are doing the right thing without insulting their book smarts.

Always be prepared to explain your practice. You don't really know something until you've successfully explained it to someone else.

September 10th

Limit coaching cues to no more than one major adaptation per set. Flooding your client's brain with every element of an elite deadlift will cause paralysis by analysis at best and an injury caused by hesitation at worst. Pick one major effort to emphasize per set and let them put in the time with it. Focus on another cue another time.

Returning to the topic of coaching cues, it is important to allow your clients an opportunity to work on one thing at a time.

They may be your client, but they are still a human, complete with the inability to truly multi-task. You must honor this with your coaching methods, focusing on only one major element at a time.

For example, telling a client that they need to "push their knees out," "keep their chest up," "pull the bar onto their back," and "exhale on the way up" might just confuse them.

Instead, choose one specific adaptation and let them nail it down until it becomes second nature. Only then should you move toward another cue or tactic.

September 11th

If your client is not taking to your coaching cues and isn't responding well to an exercise or modality, don't be stubborn. Regress the movement to a new modality or break it down into its parts. Never assume it's your client's fault and instead coach to where they are in that moment. Communicate with who you are training and not who you want to be training.

Sometimes what you're doing just isn't working. The client might be distracted, the exercise might be a bit too hard, or the coaching might not be right. Regardless, you need to know when to make an adaptation and turn a clear miss into a success.

Forcing exercises on a client is one way that many trainers violate this principle. Always pick an appropriate modality and variation of an exercise for your client's specific needs.

Another way is not being prepared with possible regressions and "cut-ups" that allow you to emphasize a simpler exercise or pieces of the greater exercise until you get to mastery. Be adaptable: it's what you are paid for.

September 12th

For every single exercise that is in your program, have a progression and a regression in mind in case things go exceptionally well or worse than expected. Even the best coaches overshoot or undersell their clients when they write the initial program. Adaptability is key.

In American football, they call it an "audible." It's a term to describe a play that wasn't called by the coach but rather by the quarterback at the line of scrimmage after seeing how the defense lined up.

The quarterback could be stubborn and try to succeed against a defense that looks prepared for him, or he can call an audible and call the right play to expose the defense's weakness.

Be that quarterback in your session. Have multiple progressions and regressions ready for the exercises in your program so that you are prepared if your client brings you something you didn't expect.

Be ready for the days they must go slow and the ones where there are no limits. Preparation is how you win games as a coach.

September 13th

Always have substitutions in mind for prime-time hours in commercial clubs. Crowds will immediately flock to the common equipment that is most easily understood and might block you from using it. Understand other ways to accomplish your goal so that your client isn't sharing equipment or waiting for you to figure out what you are going to do.

A trainer should always be prepared for what their gym floor might present, especially at busy commercial clubs. There are always those members who can spend ten minutes on a piece of equipment and refuse to allow you to work in.

Be ready to adapt for the benefit of your client. Have options available in your program in case the piece of equipment you'd like is taken.

A program that calls for a barbell bench could easily switch to an incline barbell bench or a dumbbell variation. The core concept (a loaded horizontal push) is the same.

Your client will be impressed that you can think on your feet and still get them results.

September 14th

Clients may struggle with a piece of equipment, such as a barbell or kettlebells. Whether it's a psychological or physical block isn't the point. A great coach can utilize any tool to get the job done. Don't marry yourself to any specific equipment and don't think that any one piece of equipment is so much better than the next.

It is always important to remember that equipment is just a tool that someone could use to get a job done. In the case of fitness, we don't have to worry about lacking a variety of tools—there are so many that do the same thing.

In the case of training equipment, your clients may not love how it feels to hold a piece of equipment, such as a kettlebell. Many people don't like the pressure on the back of their forearm while doing a traditional lift. Other people don't like the feeling that they aren't in control while on a treadmill.

Your job isn't to change their mind; it's to try and meet them where they are and help them achieve their training goals. Adapt your style in a way that honors what works but respects what your client can and can't do.

September 15th

We all have good days and bad days. Understand that your clients may need to be coached differently one day from the next. Life's troubles don't just disappear when someone walks into the gym. Your coaching style should pick up on the subtle changes in a personality. Be light when the time calls for it.

Always be prepared for the variation in your client's moods and capabilities. While you shouldn't bend for every single frustration or celebration in their lives, it is important to react to the big things.

A client who isn't sleeping well because of a newborn at home shouldn't be forced to stick with their high intensity program if they come in looking like the walking dead. Instead, you should be ready to modify some intensity out and focus on movement quality, tissue regeneration, or some other variable.

Just the same, a client may come to you hours after some great news or moments after a powerful coffee. Be ready to use this energy for their benefit. Push them a bit harder, within their normal program, and give them the opportunity to progress themselves.

September 16th

Look to string together multiple movement patterns that work similar contexts in the body. For example, one session may have the hinge, core stability, and overhead press while another emphasizes knee-dominant movements, rotational core, and horizontal pull. Thinking in terms of "linking" movements enhances learning capabilities.

A successful training session is one that has a tremendous amount of flow to it. The organization of your exercises, circuits, and rest periods should tie together seamlessly, creating a flow state that your client can settle into.

This is best accomplished by putting together exercises that share commonalities but do not directly compete. For example, a loaded hinge pattern goes well with an overhead push because both work stability of the core (anti-flexion and anti-extension) but do not share similar active muscles.

This sort of organization allows a client to work at higher intensities without feeling overtaxed, providing more results and a better training experience.

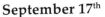

September 17th

Give a brief preview of the day's session as your client begins their standard mobility and movement preparation work. By giving them the layout of the workout, they'll be able to prepare more optimally for the physical and psychological demands.

Every major movie that hits theatres does so with a myriad of preview clips already released to the public. Obviously, this draws attention and can increase profits, but it also helps prepare moviegoers for what they're about to see.

Give this same courtesy to your clients by taking them through the day's tasks as they work through some of their warm-up. Detail your plan while they roll out and highlight the finisher long before you get to the end.

Your client will appreciate the opportunity to mentally prepare for the physical task. Like a football player knowing what will be asked of them on a given play, more information can lead to a better performance.

Set your clients up to succeed by letting them in on the plan for the day.

September 18th

Trainers tend to fall into two categories: too little programming that leads to extra time at the end or too much programming that leads to a scramble. Regardless of which title applies to you, separate your workout into two categories: mandatory movements and optional work. Ensure the mandatory work is done each session, but the optional is available if you have the time.

A training session must be treated differently from an abstract "workout." For one, there should be a specific focus and outcome to every session. But also realize that your client is paying for a fixed amount of a time.

In knowing these two factors, you are equipped with enough knowledge to design your programs appropriately. Every session should contain movements that are mandatory (the ones that achieve the specific focus) and others that can add fun, intensity, or variety.

Always emphasize your mandatory movements and save other, less critical things for the days when your client is working at an exceptional pace or needs the change-up.

September 19th

When introducing a new exercise, aim to achieve the triad of learning. Demonstration for the visual, description for the auditory, and relating it to something they already understand for the memory recall. When you can hit all three centers of learning, you are more likely to create a successful experience for your client, no matter how complex the task.

The art of coaching cannot be separated from the art of learning. A coach is only as good as their understanding of learning.

Your clients learn by watching you, hearing you, and trying something themselves. They also learn by making connections between old, well-understood actions and new ones.

Do your best to honor all of these learning modalities when instructing your clients. Tell them what they are going to do while you show them. Then, take the time to relate it to something they've done before with phrases such as, "This is just like *x*." Lastly, let them learn with their own bodies.

Coaching is an art that requires all of your senses.

September 20th

Some movements, such as the power clean, will never appear in a program for a client. Yet, a client may express a desire to do them. This puts you in a precarious position, one which asks you to take care of your client's wants but also to remain a professional and do what is best. Always emphasize safety, yet look to meet them halfway, such as creating a similar effect with another piece of equipment.

As a coach, you must occasionally play the role of stop sign, that is, being the reason someone doesn't hurt themselves (on your watch).

Many clients will overestimate their abilities. They will reference previous trainers, their past athletic accomplishments, or a video they saw on Instagram. Your job is to wade through this hubris and remain committed to the best course of action:

Programming and coaching the exercises your client can do safely and effectively.

With that said, look to find ways to compromise with your clients to satisfy their desire for more while honoring your commitment to safe and specific programming. Negotiate the best course of action.

September 21st

Programming in a touch of client freedom at the end of a workout can create the level of fun that many clients need to push through the hard parts. Hammering out meters on a rower or sprints on a treadmill create similar metabolic effects, so let them choose their path.

Free will is the greatest gift the human species possesses. We are not completely trapped by our animalistic instincts or an overwhelming drive for survival.

Instead, we are often allowed opportunities to make decisions and to potentially change the course of our (and others') lives. This freedom is a satisfying gift that should be appreciated.

On the other hand, exercise programs tend to be very stiff. They're what the coach designed for the day and nothing more. This is both admirable and pompous.

The world will not explode if you allow the final few minutes of every training session to be dictated by your clients. Design your programs to have two or three options that your clients can choose from (never to be repeated in back-to-back sessions).

This sort of ownership can make your clients that much happier with you and your training practice.

September 22nd

Being a personal trainer often leads to becoming a personal therapist for many clients. Embrace this role but understand your limitations and expertise. Listen intently and provide your thoughts when appropriate, but never prescribe a behavior or advise someone to handle a situation in their personal life that may have major consequences.

Spend enough quality time around someone and eventually they'll begin to open up to you. Most clients will limit the depth that they dive to on personal matters and details of their lives. Others will spend your entire session discussing their problems.

It is always good to listen and be a good ear, but it is critical to understand two important rules:

1. Know your lane. Unless you are a psychologist or therapist, you'll want to avoid giving advice or prompting action in your clients' lives.
2. You are a personal trainer, a job that puts you in a position to make someone exercise for the length of a session. You must try to do your job and keep your clients on task.

Always listen, but know your role and honor it.

September 23rd

If you are certified to provide nutrition advice to your clients, it can be tempting to provide feedback during a training session. Instead, schedule time to meet where there are no sets to complete and no heart rate to maintain. You'll still bill the hour you meet with a client for nutrition as though it were a training session, but you'll be able to focus entirely on the topic.

Being able to provide multiple services is a definite way to attract and retain business. Humans love convenience. We love being able to be as efficient as possible.

However, it is important to separate your services into their own hours. Doing so allows you to bill each uniquely while ensuring that you are maximizing your attention on one thing at a time.

You probably notice that your clients would prefer receiving nutrition advice in between sets of their exercises, which is a practice far too many trainers engage in.

You and your client will benefit from being able to maximize the effectiveness of each session type by staying on topic and delivering optimal results for that hour.

September 24ᵗʰ

Ask for client feedback on your program at the end of the session while highlighting what you felt went well. Mutual feedback allows both the coach and the trainee to feel appreciated and provides a driving force to keep moving forward. It doesn't need to be profound, but it helps if your clients feel as though they can comfortably voice their thoughts on their workouts. They are paying for it after all.

Far too often in personal training, we abruptly end our sessions with a high-five and a "see you next time" sort of comment. There is certainly nothing wrong with this, but there are ways to make it better.

Spending some time to review what has been done in the session that day is an excellent way to communicate to a client that you care.

The sort of review also allows you to ask your client for their opinion on what was done. You'll understand how they received your training session, which is critical information for you to continue getting better at your job.

September 25th

Some movements elude people, especially if they've been inactive for a while. Avoid the frustration that comes with failure to meet demands and explain how many sessions it may take to "master" a movement. For example, it may take five or six sessions to completely own the hinge pattern while the biceps curl can be handled in five minutes. Explain the complexity of a movement and how common it is for someone to need time to figure it out before letting them experience it.

Fitness is not an easy ball game. Even refined fitness professionals can struggle mastering new concepts and movements with their bodies, so imagine how it feels to be one of your recently motivated, but previously inactive, clients.

Some people will struggle greatly when trying to master a new movement pattern while others will struggle just to get to a level of adequacy. These individuals can get frustrated and want to throw in the proverbial towel, especially if they are successful in many other endeavors in their lives.

Avoid this conflict and frustration by taking the time to explain to your clients just how intricate and complex the movements you are teaching them really are.

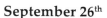

September 26th

No one coach is so great that they can teach everything. Understand the value in bringing in outside opinions from fellow coaches for your clients. Showing humility and a genuine desire for your clients to grow doesn't hurt your brand—it helps it. It's tough, but if you know someone you associate with is the best, why wouldn't you leverage them?

One of the worst mistakes a professional in any field can make is presenting themselves as the foremost authority on everything in the realm of their profession. It seems like the logical thing to do to attract business and impress people, but it can damage your reputation much more than improve it.

Picture this: a client with a specific issue comes to you for training. In your puff of confidence, you tell them that you can handle anything. Later, your client learns that you work with someone who is *known* for their specialization in their issue. They ask if you have consulted with them and you say no.

How do you think that client feels? Might they worry that your arrogance is blinding you from getting them the results that they are paying you for?

September 27th

Don't lie to your clients. Not just about the obvious stuff your mother cautioned you against, but also the time they are working, how many repetitions are left, or how much weight is loaded up. Trust is a serious aspect of the trainer-client relationship and must be present for the client to excel.

Trust is not easy to acquire in human transactions that involve money. There are ways of faking it, as is taught in many sales lectures, but a personal trainer should never do this.

Always be honest and up front with your clients. It isn't funny to tell them they are going to work hard for thirty seconds, only to drag it out to forty-five. Don't tell your clients that they are only lifting x pounds when in fact you've loaded the bar much beyond that.

These sorts of antics do not make you a better trainer because you are "pushing people past their limits." To the contrary, it makes you a horrible trainer who must use gimmicks and trickery to gain client compliance.

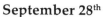

September 28th

*Integrating your client with the culture of your gym
and the people within it is always a great idea. Community
is one of the strongest influences in human development.
Placing a client within a well-oiled community of
like-minded individuals will pay off in the short
term and long term.*

Community is one of the most motivating factors for us as humans. Each one of us wants to feel as though we belong to something. Whether it's a book club that meets at a local library, a bus full of fans heading to a football tailgate, or the members of your fitness facility forming a bond after a workout, these communities hold tremendous power.

For example, sometimes your client won't want to work out with you. They'll have had a bad day, a busy day, or would rather lie on the couch and watch Netflix. If they communicate only with you this might be easy to do. But if they've been introduced to the client who trains before them and they know who trains after, along with other faces of your gym, they'll feel an obligation to show up.

Be the person who improves your client's life by improving their fitness and expanding their social network. We are all in this together, after all.

September 29th

Coaching is an art. There is no one right way, but there are plenty of wrong ways. In almost any setting, belittling your client, yelling at them, or creating no-win scenarios just for the sake of sweat are not great coaching tactics. Be above the swamp of bad professionals and create a healthy environment for your clients.

It seems like there's another type of story that becomes breaking news every few months: a coach is filmed assaulting his players, overheard belittling his athletes, or worse, pushing them to the point of health-risk.

These incidents are not isolated to the sporting world or the gritty training grounds of military institutions.

Sadly, many trainers in the fitness industry think it's OK to break down their clients. They tear down people physically, emotionally, and spiritually, all while charging them for it.

You can push your clients quite hard without ever insulting them. You can challenge them without invoking fear. You can break down their bodies so long as you promise to be there to help them build it back up.

You must coach with empathy and love.

September 30th

Study coaches of all different disciplines. Sports, business, fitness, and even music teachers all have something to say about how humans learn best. Understanding the variety of methods and tactics that are available for use only makes you a better coach. A quote from a business coach may just help you better explain a squat.

Coaching is an art that has no borders. If you can coach a young athlete to kick a ball into a soccer goal, then you could probably coach someone to improve their financial status, assuming you've invested the time and effort to understand either discipline.

Coaching, at its core, is about understanding people, emotions, and learning principles. It isn't necessarily about a subject matter. Sure, being a PhD in a given topic implies that you yourself have absorbed a ton of information about something specific, but it doesn't mean that you are capable of imparting that wisdom onto someone else.

Study the methods of coaches around the world. You'll soon notice that the best ones do this:

Listen with the intent to learn, think with the intent to coach, and coach with the intent to cause change in the person.

October

Definitions and Common Terms

"October is the fallen leaf, but it is also a wider horizon more clearly seen. It is the distant hills once more in sight, and the enduring constellations above them once again."

—Hal Borland

"Most controversies would soon be ended, if those engaged in them would first accurately define their terms, and then adhere to their definitions."

—Tryon Edwards

October 1st

Progressive overload is the cornerstone of personal training. Often spoken about in relation to the load of an exercise, progressive overload suggests that you will gradually increase intensity over time to overload the muscles and maintain a level of consistent growth. Realize though that progressive overload can also apply to coordination, speed, endurance, and cardiovascular fitness.

There is one principle, above all others, that must be honored in personal training, and it is progressive overload. The reason it must be honored is quite simple:

It's how the body adapts.

Take anything in life: lifting weights, learning Spanish, or mastering your first dance for your upcoming wedding. You must learn it piece by piece.

Just as the greatest skyscrapers must be completed one floor at a time, all great physical feats must be done on the solid foundation set before it. So, whether you are training your client to lift heavier weights, run faster miles, or simply look better and live healthier, you must do so in a manner that is "brick by brick."

October 2nd

*Specific Adaptations to Imposed Demands (SAID)
suggests that whatever stress is placed upon a body will be
met with a specific adaptation. For example, consistent
application of external load (weight training) will cause
an increase in the cross-sectional area of muscle fibers
involved, calcification of the bony processes that connect
to tendons, and an increased efficiency of ATP/CP and
glycolytic energy systems. The body will adapt very
specifically to whatever demand is placed upon it.*

The body is an intelligent system designed for survival. With this fact in mind, we must acknowledge that it doesn't necessarily "want" additional muscle mass, Herculean strength, or seemingly unlimited endurance capacities.

These sorts of achievements require an overriding of the body's homeostasis. Thus, any training stimulus you place upon your clients must be specific to the adaptations that are sought after.

An avid runner desperate to gain some muscle mass back and strengthen their hips must decrease their running for a while to ensure their body switches to muscle-building mode.

October 3rd

*Volume is a consideration of repetitions, sets, and load
of a given exercise or session. A person lifting one hundred
pounds for three sets of ten repetitions will do three
thousand pounds of volume on that given exercise.
It's important to know the volume of your prescribed work
to ensure clients are not overtraining during sessions or
are given adequate rest between high volume sessions.*

Training volume is a concept that has been in the vocabulary of bodybuilding and strength coaches for quite some time. Yet, many personal trainers aren't equipped with a proper understanding of what volume is, why it matters, and how to manipulate it.

In short, training volume is the amount of work (Load x Reps x Sets). Training volume can be changed by manipulating (up or down) any of those three variables.

In personal training, a gradual increase in training volume over time is a great sign of progress. However, most clients aren't going to reach absurd training volumes. Instead, these clients need moderate volume and high frequency for success.

October 4th

*Density is volume with the addition of time as a variable.
If someone can do three thousand pounds of work in
ten minutes, we'd find their density to be three hundred
pounds per minute. Extrapolating this outward over
an entire circuit of movements, or the session, can help
us improve the work-to-time ratio of our clients, which
is a great measure of fitness.*

Density is a natural expansion on volume. With density, we are simply dividing our volume total by the amount of time we are working.

This formula makes density the most important variable to tackle for personal trainers. Our time is usually fixed (thirty- or sixty-minute sessions), thus giving us a number to divide our volume against.

A great fitness goal for nearly all clients is to increase their exercise density on a given program. In the beginning, it may take them all sixty minutes to complete the prescribed volume of work you have programmed. At the end of that six weeks they may be doing it in forty-five—a very impressive improvement of their muscular and cardiovascular endurance capacity.

Improving someone's workout density will have a tremendous impact on their overall fitness.

October 5th

Periodization is the practice of breaking down a program into phases that emphasize one or two fitness qualities at a time. For example, a bodybuilder might enter a strength phase for six to eight weeks, followed by a hypertrophy phase for ten to twelve. The goal would be to improve their force production capability prior to emphasizing muscle growth and development. All great coaches utilize the concept of periodization in their programs.

Every coach and trainer should have a thoughtful program for their clients: one that considers the unique aspects of the individual and the training stimuli needed to achieve their goals.

Going one step further, every trainer should understand how to periodize their program into blocks of time.

Each block is built around a specific training stimulus (relating back to the SAID principle) and runs for a period of six to twelve weeks. These blocks are then stacked together in succession to build out an entire year's worth of programming.

Blocks should be designed to transition into each other, providing a seamless training experience.

October 6th

The sagittal plane is the most common movement plane utilized in the gym. Whether you are deadlifting, running on a treadmill, or doing biceps curls in the mirror, you are working in the sagittal plane.

The three planes of motion are an often-overlooked element in personal training programs. It can feel like information overload when you sit down and begin writing out a client's program. You must factor the major movement patterns, the correctives for their dysfunctions, you want to improve their definition, burn off the fat, and make them happy.

And now you must think about movement planes?

Training someone through multiple planes is imperative for improving athletic performance, ensuring muscular balance, correcting mobility and stability issues, and creating strong neurological connections across our three segments.

The sagittal plane, for example, splits the body into its left and right halves as though a line went from our forehead to the floor. This means that any exercise in the sagittal plane only considers the left and right aspects of our body.

October 7th

The frontal plane is an often-forgotten plane of movement in the common exercise program. Moving side-to-side, such as in a lateral lunge or a lateral dumbbell raise, is critical for the development of the abductor and adductor capabilities of the hip and shoulder joints. It's important to incorporate this plane in every program to address the function of joints.

Some trainers struggle most to work the frontal plane into their programs. Beyond lateral lunging and traditional dumbbell side raises, they struggle to find movements that address it.

Picture a line that runs from the top of your head, down your sides/arms and all the way down your legs to the floor, essentially cutting you into a front and back half. This is the frontal plane.

It's crucial to work the body in this manner because it involves the body moving laterally through space, which can be confusing considering we call it "the frontal plane."

Exercises such as the Cossack squat, shuffling pallof press hold, mini-band walks, and even jumping jacks exist here. Be sure to use it and allow the body to communicate in this critical plane.

October 8th

The transverse plane is all about rotation. Whether it is a medicine ball throw, a wood chop on a cable, or picking up your foot and rotating your body between repetitions of goblet squats, it is imperative to experience exercise in three dimensions. The utilization of rotation patterns is essential to optimal development of your client's skillset, especially in athletic populations.

The final plane involves cutting the body in half at the waist, giving us an upper and lower segment. It is this "cut" that helps us best understand how the transverse plane works.

Think of a baseball player swinging a bat. First there's a frontal plane movement as they lift the front foot from the ground and stride toward the baseball.

The transverse element comes into play when the upper segment begins twisting while the lower holds steady to preserve power and maintain stability.

In the gym, utilize wood chops and anti-rotation movements to mimic this exact pattern. Rotational lunges and squats and even pushups are also transverse exercises.

Unlock your programs and use all three planes.

October 9ᵗʰ

Hypertrophy, or the act of building muscle tissue, is a training goal for a large population of people who exercise. It is important to understand that the primary stimulus for muscle growth is not how much weight you lift per se, but rather the amount of time that a working muscle stays engaged with a tension (time-under-tension). Tempo involving a load that is moderate serves this goal better than high load and high velocity.

An increase in lean body mass, specifically muscle, is a goal of just about every client you will ever work with. For some it is the obvious, outward goal: they hired you because they want bigger muscles. Others will want to lose body fat and look better in the mirror, which is something that increased muscle mass greatly helps with, considering the effects on basal metabolic rate, force production, and body definition.

Study the details behind hypertrophy and you realize that it isn't just achieved by lifting heavy weights, nor is it necessarily achieved by thrashing the body repeatedly. Rather, concentrated repetitions executed with a slower concentric/eccentric tempo break down tissue in a way that signals the body to build additional mass.

Create the effects your clients need.

October 10th

Lipolysis, or the act of burning fat, is the most common training goal for people. The human metabolism is never burning carbohydrates or fats exclusively, but its activity level and output are factors that can increase the level of fat-burning that occurs. Intense bouts of exercise that create a large deficit of oxygen will have an after-burn effect that helps clients burn calories even after they finish. Utilizing fat as energy also comes from not providing the body enough carbohydrates to fuel the production of glucose and glycogen, which has led to the popularity of low-carbohydrate dieting.

Just about everyone who would consider your services would appreciate a loss of body fat. For some it may be a secondary goal to something else. For most though, it will be their primary focus, and one they're hiring you to help them accomplish.

Burning fat is much more specific than hard workouts and calorie-restricted diets. Millions of dollars are spent each year studying the science of lipolysis and there still isn't "one secret" to rule them all.

You don't need to read every piece of literature, but you should be familiar with the many pathways the body uses to burn fat for energy.

October 11th

EPOC (Excess Post-Exercise Oxygen Consumption) is the idea that a period of exercise creates an oxygen deficit that must be repaid. In the hours and even days (depending on intensity) after a training session, a client could be still burning calories to recover. An optimal strategy for weight loss utilizes this phenomenon to a client's advantage.

There are a variety of systems in the body that can be triggered in an advantageous way. EPOC is one of those systems.

At its simplest level, it's a process that is used by the body to recapture all the oxygen that was lost from the body during exercise. Moreover, many cells must undergo repair, a mechanical makeover to improve the integrity of the cell.

All this work and the oversaturation of oxygen in the body has a caloric cost, and a high one that requires stored fat for fuel.

For this reason, an intense bout of exercise, whether it's heavy resistance training or interval cardio, can burn calories for many hours after its completion. Have your clients stack their workouts, with you and on their own, to keep this "afterburn" going indefinitely.

October 12ᵗʰ

*Muscles have two significant fiber types that every trainer
should understand. Type I fibers are capable of lower
force output but can last much longer during exercise.
These characteristics are often associated with marathon
running. Meanwhile, type II fibers have a higher force
output but aren't capable of resisting fatigue very well.
A powerlifter would be a great example of someone who
has optimized their type II fibers.*

One of the scientific principles that is mandatory learning for a fitness professional is muscle fiber types. You cannot successfully design and execute a training program without knowing what you are doing regarding working muscles.

This is especially important for clients who are looking to improve their strength and power, which are physical attributes that require lifting protocols that emphasize type II fibers. A program that doesn't provide this essential stimulus will be incapable of improving these attributes.

Other goal types are impacted too. Everyone from bodybuilders to marathon runners must have training programs that consider the specificity of their sports and goals.

October 13th

Acceleration is an element of force creation that can't be overlooked. Negative acceleration, or deceleration, is something a coach should be mindful of. Are your clients handling the forces of stopping motion as well as they are handling the stress of creating them? Utilizing a variety of loading methods can allow for acceleration to be trained. Lower loads will have greater velocity.

Mechanical force is not constant. Everything from an elite sprinter to a rocket ship must accelerate from one velocity to a greater one. NASA utilizes high-grade fuels to create combustion reactions that propel the ship into space.

Humans also require an intricate series of events to occur if they are to accelerate. The muscles, fascia, joints, cardiovascular system, and the nervous system are all in involved. Deceleration requires the same level of connectivity but creates even greater stress on the structures of the body.

For this very reason, we must train this skill in all our clients. It will look very different when we work with an elderly client than with a collegiate athlete. Still, we must honor the body's need to accelerate and decelerate for surviving and thriving purposes.

October 14th

The eccentric contraction is the most stressful on the body when compared to the concentric and isometric movements. It is common to confuse the effort it takes to move a weight toward your center or mass, or stabilize a load in a singular space, with being harder on the body, but loaded stretching of the muscle fibers (the eccentric phase) damages more muscle fibers and can lead to greater delayed onset muscle soreness.

Research into the intricate relationships between myosin and actin overlap (the sliding filament theory) has shown interesting data regarding the phases of muscular contraction.

The concentric phase requires an acceleration of a mass to occur while fibers begin overlapping to form cross-bridges. An isometric contraction requires the maintenance of the cross-bridges and consistent tension across a working muscle. Damage is greatest during the eccentric phase of an exercise due to the tearing of these cross-bridges as the muscle returns to length.

Understanding this phenomenon allows you to push your most advanced clients and limit the soreness in those who are newer to exercise.

October 15th

Effort during concentric contraction is directly related to the distance a load must travel. A seven-foot basketball player trying to squat does significantly more work than someone who is five-foot-five. The same phenomenon even takes place in a biceps curl. Longer limbs create longer arcs.

It should go without saying that people's biomechanics will change as their body size changes. There are costs and benefits to our heights, widths, and weights, regardless of which end of the spectrum a person finds themselves on.

For example, an individual with longer limbs will do more work during the concentric portion of a lift than someone who has much shorter limbs. This is because they must make the weight travel a greater distance, which is an increased cost on the body's metabolic and muscular capabilities.

Knowing this can guide your programming as a trainer as you work with people in a variety of shapes and sizes. Short-armed people tend to crush horizontal push patterns while a longer-armed individual is likely better at chin-ups than pull-ups.

Your programming must account for these differences.

October 16th

The Seven Major Movement patterns are horizontal pull and push, vertical pull and push, hip dominant, knee dominant, and rotation. Be sure to incorporate each pattern in all your programs. These patterns are the core element to every exercise in the gym and should be the cornerstone of all your programs. Mastering these base movements is critical before progressing onto advanced variations of exercises.

Personal training, at its simplest, is increasing movement frequency, integrity, and variety in a client. It isn't building muscle, burning fat, or any of the other myriad goals that come our way.

You may balk at this notion initially. You may be thinking, "My job is to get my clients in the best shape of their lives," "I am a life-changer," or "I do more than that." A genuine salute for your conviction and dedication is deserved.

But at its core, our job is to become masters of human movement, which qualifies us to help others become masters of it too (at least for themselves). For that reason, all your programs must include the seven basic movement patterns in some way. Each pattern should be done loaded and unloaded, assisted and resisted, and throughout all three planes.

Day by Day

October 17th

Self-Myofascial Release is a popular method for improving the mobility of clients. It is important to understand that the purpose is only to increase blood flow prior to training a movement. Most SMR is not capable of breaking up fascia or scar tissue. It does not go deep enough in the body. Instead, emphasize how it will help a client find mobility in a joint due to increased blood flow to the region, perfect prior to a session where tightness could be limiting a person from performing an exercise correctly.

Self-myofascial release and other musculofascial integrity intervention methods are all the rage in the fitness industry now. Rightfully so, too. It is critical to work our bodies not just with intense exercise but to also help them recover with modalities meant to increase blood flow, improve joint mobility, lower cortisol, and find new functionality.

However, we must remember that SMR and other methods do not replace a qualified physical therapist, a licensed massage therapist, or an orthopedic doctor. In fact, we must always honor our role as trainers by referring up to these positions and never making claims that would put our professional integrity at risk.

October 18th

VO$_2$ max is a measure of a client's absolute cardiovascular output. Establishing this value early in an assessment process can allow for you to prescribe percentage-based cardiovascular workouts that are designed to move a client toward their goals. However, this assessment is not always possible in gym settings, so other methods such as the Bruce Protocol can be utilized to get rough estimates of the VO$_2$ max.

Cardiovascular output is a critical element of human survival. We should always aim to understand just how well our clients can function under normal and stressful scenarios (exercise counts as a stress here). This helps us ensure we always prescribe safe and effective training methods for our clients.

Going a step further though, specific tests such as VO$_2$ max allow us to see the absolute capabilities of our clients who seek that information. This would be an example of training to "thrive" versus training to "survive."

Gathering data on our high-performance clients can allow us to design even more specific programs meant to create specific effects in our clients. More data about your clients' abilities helps you deliver a better service and better results.

October 19th

The anaerobic threshold is a critical point in a client's metabolism. This is the point at which the ability to buffer hydrogen out of a working muscle has been exceeded by the demand. It is at this moment that the "burn" becomes noticeable. Moving this value to the right, as if you were looking at a line graph, is a sign of increased anaerobic capacity. Training endurance sets (above fifteen repetitions) can aid in this. It should be noted that the "burn" is not lactic acid itself, but the accumulation of hydrogen ions in the working tissue.

It could be argued that anaerobic threshold is one of the most critical physiological phenomena in the body (regarding exercise). This piece of data, "AT," points to the moment when our client's body can no longer buffer out hydrogen ions from working muscles at a rate that matches the intensity of exercise.

When you "feel the burn," the body begins to lose its ability to function anaerobically, thus causing it to dip into aerobic energy production or cease exercise for a moment. This factor has an impact on high repetition muscular endurance and even strength endurance (how long someone can lift a specific percentage of max load before needing to drop load).

October 20th

Dynamic posture is the ability to get in and out of specific positions as a reaction to an outside stimulus. Static posture is one's "walking around" posture. Establishing that some joint actions or positions are acceptable for dynamic posture but not acceptable for static posture is key to unlocking a client's athletic potential while maintaining a healthy neutral state.

In recent years, the movement toward functional training has increased the attention that is paid to posture. For good reason, too. Poor posture has been shown to have an impact on everything from injury risk to life span.

Still though, far too many people have come to understand posture as a static state of being, as if the body should never leave an erect position with neutral hips, retracted and depressed scapulae, tucked chin, drawn-in abdominals, and balanced weight through the middle of the feet.

Our posture, like life, must be dynamic. There must be elements of anterior and posterior pelvic tilt just as the shoulders should be able to *gasp* protract.

Create differentiation in your mind (and your clients') between static and dynamic posture positions.

October 21st

The core musculature involves more than just the rectus abdominis and the obliques, the common show muscles on magazine covers. Training the pelvic floor, the transverse abdominis, the serratus anterior, and even the glutes is critical to providing clients a stable and durable core. Its function is as a conduit for force throughout the body. And while it could be chiseled and attractive, it's important to decipher the core's purpose apart from our typical interpretation.

The "core" has evolved from being a region of the body to becoming another trendy buzzword that fills the vocabulary of trainers and fitness enthusiasts everywhere. Everyone is training it.

But we must return to the basic function of said "core." The muscles of the core are designed to be force transducers above all else. This means that the core's primary function is to contract isometrically so that the limbs may exert high levels of force.

Knocking out another set of crunches or leg raises isn't going to cut it. Instead, a program built on deep breathing, core stability (anti-movements), and control of the pelvis by the glutes is best.

Train the core's "core" functions over vanity.

October 22nd

Fascial tissue has been recently identified as an organ capable of communicating millions of bits of data in short spans of time throughout the body. Acknowledging this marvel is critical in the design of your exercise programs since movement should always take priority over muscle contraction. Getting someone to lift a load from one foot to the opposite shoulder, with proper form, is significantly more beneficial than another set of shoulder or arm exercises.

Any personal trainer worth their salary should be doing their best to understand the amazing nature of fascial tissue. This once overlooked, still underappreciated part of the body is capable of translating millions of data points in seconds in seemingly impossible ways.

Elite athletic accomplishments are not just the result of muscular contractions and joint movements. No, many incredible feats of human performance are achieved because the fascia has taken tension from one sling and applied it to another.

Study fascial slings and begin integrating loaded and unloaded movements that challenge these slings in your programs. No matter who your client is, what they are training for, or how good they are at training, they can benefit tremendously.

October 23nd

Ketosis is a popular dieting strategy to employ with clients because a body without adequate blood sugar will begin converting proteins and fats into ketones, which feed and fuel the body instead. This can be a powerful strategy for someone who is ready to not only eat fewer carbohydrates and more fats but is also capable of self-monitoring their health markers to ensure that they are safe. Ketosis is not a beginner's method and should not be used with significantly overweight clients until they've established sustainable habits for health.

Once again, another low carbohydrate diet strategy has grabbed the hearts, minds, and waistlines of American fitness professionals, fitness enthusiasts, and weight loss hopefuls. Every few years, another version of this proven method of dietary intervention becomes the newest fad.

Ketosis does work for many people because it forces the body to begin using alternate sources of fuel to create blood glucose. For those who do it right, this usually means increased lipolysis.

However, most of your clients aren't ready for such intense protocols. For most, basic nutrition intervention will do the trick and create inspiring results.

October 24th

*Carbohydrate loading is the practice of ingesting forty
to eighty grams of simple sugars prior to exercise with
the intent of filling blood glucose stores for optimized
performance. Elite athletes may even carbohydrate load
days in advance to increase muscle and liver glycogen
levels. This topic is complex and exact amounts depend
on a individual's physical condition, the demands of
the activity, and normal dietary structure.*

On the opposite end of the spectrum of ketosis we
have carbohydrate loading: a method for improving
performance by increasing the amount of fuel that is
available for consumption during exercise.

For many elite athletes, it's the difference between their
best performance and a mediocre effort. When done
correctly, you can effectively supercharge the body's
cells with glucose, glycogen, and water, which are all
critical elements of ATP production.

Still though, it's an advanced eating technique that
doesn't tend to work well in the hands of people who
are new to dieting or exercising with intensity. This
is because many people will use a loading period as a
justification to overeat, to eat junk and call it fuel, or to
increase overall calories regardless of activity levels. Be
sure you know your clients.

October 25th

Mobility is the ability of a bone to move throughout an optimal range of motion at a joint, whereas flexibility is the relative tension, or lack thereof, between the two end points of a given muscle. A client who is new to exercise should emphasize mobility prior to flexibility. Gaining access to an optimal range of motion will often lead to appropriate adaptations in muscular flexibility. We shouldn't spend time stretching tight muscles when immobility or lack of strength is the real issue.

All too often, these terms are used interchangeably. Flexibility is not mobility and mobility is not flexibility. It is imperative for fitness professionals to know the difference.

Mobility is the available range of motion at a joint in question, such as the hip during a Cossack squat. Having great flexibility in the hamstrings and adductors can go a long way toward reaching optimal position, but mobility specifically refers to the function of the femur externally rotating in the hip socket.

Improving someone's flexibility is about removing unnecessary tension from muscle bellies by combining stretching, myofascial release techniques, and functional movement patterns into their program.

October 26th

Body fat percentage is a two-part variable. You can make body fat percentage decrease by either gaining muscle or losing fat. Don't assume that every person with a non-optimal body fat percentage needs to lose weight. Many people could benefit greatly from the 5-10 exchange: a five-pound increase in muscle tissue and a ten-pound decrease in fat mass. This could equate to about a three to five percent change in the reading, depending on the overall size of the individual being tested.

For many people, the focus is on weight loss. And to some degree, that's right. If most people were to lose six to ten pounds, especially in fat, then they'd also see a dramatic improvement in their health.

Yet, when we focus in on body fat percentage, we need to remember that it's a variable with two key data points: fat mass and lean mass.

Many clients are going to assume that they need only to lose weight to achieve their dream body, although an assessment might reveal they need to increase their lean body mass by five to ten pounds.

Remember, you are the expert who is being paid to deliver results. Don't be swayed by a client's words when your assessments show a different story.

October 27th

Inertia is the law of motion that states that an object at rest will remain at rest until acted upon by an outside force that can overcome it. This is why a deadlift can feel so much heavier in the first few inches of the pull. The law also states that an object in motion wants to stay in motion until it is acted upon by an outside force that can overcome it, which is why it can feel so hard to stop a descending barbell in a heavy squat or press.

A common flaw in many trainers' knowledge base is that they're missing basic physics. This isn't a shortcoming of the trainer per se but rather a reflection of the gaps in the common certifications. Physics governs all that we do in the gym, so we should spend time understanding certain principles.

With inertia, remember that it has two principles:

1. Objects at rest want to stay at rest, and
2. Objects in motion want to stay in motion

These two rules explain why deadlifts can feel so heavy compared to squats and why deceleration out of a plyometric exercise must be done appropriately to absorb forces the right way.

Inertia is always in play.

October 28th

A neutral spine should not be confused with a "flat spine." A neutral spine is one that observes the natural curvature found in the thoracic and lumbar spines overtop of a balanced pelvis. A flat spine, however, insinuates a posterior pelvic tilt, thoracic extension, and a packed chin, effectively straightening the spine. The former position is optimal for nearly all human movements while the latter could cause damage if misapplied.

A common miscue in personal training is telling clients to maintain a "flat spine." Anatomically speaking, a flat spine is possible, but it would not be an ideal position for clients to be in, especially for an extended period of time.

When looking at the spine, it's critical to remember that there is a natural curvature that should be present unless specific direction was given to minimize it. Each segment of the spine is meant to flex and extend, while the pelvis is designed to tilt forward and backward.

Acknowledging this allows us to see that the spine can be in a variety of positions and still be safe. It's also important to remember that laws of spinal position change when looking at loaded and unloaded movement patterns.

October 29th

The pelvic tilts are a major element of movement mastery. An anterior pelvic tilt is one from which "water" could be poured out of the front of the body, while a posterior tilt is one that pulls your belt buckle toward your nose. A neutral pelvis is optimal at rest, but movement requires a flow up and down the spectrum of anterior and posterior tilts.

Many people, especially trainers, spend a lot of time talking about the muscles of the hip. Phrases such as "build your glutes," "fire your abductors," and "strengthen your posterior chain and core" are used to describe the intent of programs and training modalities.

Little thought is given as to why we do these things. Training and strengthening specific muscles must be a part of a greater plan to improve the quality of movement: these muscles are the means to a greater end.

Studying the pelvis specifically, we see the possibility of anterior, posterior, and lateral tilts. Each of these tilt patterns, including neutral, requires the interplay of muscles and fasciae.

As a trainer, understand that your goal is to develop mastery of these patterns in each of your clients.

October 30th

"Unilateral" refers to a single limb performing a movement.
"Bilateral" refers to both limbs doing the same movement.
"Contralateral" states that opposite arms and legs are doing
a movement (such as a bird dog). Lastly, "ipsilateral"
coaches that the same-side arm and leg will act in unison.

Many great bodies have been built utilizing predominantly bilateral movements. Any movement that has all four limbs in contact with the ground and resistance is capable of exerting adequate force into working muscles.

However, training the body's limbs to work independently (unilateral) and in coordinated efforts (contralateral and ipsilateral) can lead to the realization of even greater progress. This is because by improving the neurological control of each segment of the body, you are effectively improving the strength too.

High levels of muscular coordination allow for even greater levels of force production because each unit can stabilize itself and coordinate with other segments. Once a client returns to bilateral movement, we typically see a major improvement in performance.

@

October 31st

Cortisol is the stress hormone. Exercise can decrease its levels in the blood stream, but it can also increase these levels. It's important to understand the difference between exercising for wellness and stress-relief and exercising to radically improve a specific measure. Not everyone needs, or should have, highly intense workouts.

The average person could benefit from greatly decreasing their cortisol levels, setting the stage for a better fat-burning environment.

Many trainers discuss the importance of getting adequate sleep, removing blue light, increasing exercise frequency, and eating healthier foods. However, we must remember that cortisol can be increased by our exercise programs.

Our bodies can't quite tell the difference between exercising for health and surviving a life-threatening situation. It just knows we are experiencing a higher heart rate, burning calories, and feeling stress.

Make sure a stressed-out client doesn't add more stress into their life with intense exercise programs that don't respect recovery. These individuals might need to work at a slower pace until whatever stressor in their life ceases. Intensity should match stress levels.

November

Myth Busting

"The candidate out front on Labor Day has historically been the one who stayed ahead in November."

—Peter Jennings

"The great enemy of the truth is very often not the lie, deliberate, contrived and dishonest, but the myth, persistent, persuasive and unrealistic."

—John F. Kennedy

November 1st

Flexibility has become a questionable term in fitness. Science has shown that static stretching, for many populations, offers little to no long-term benefit. While it may feel good to increase blood flow to the muscles, it's important to note that you can't lengthen a muscle unless you detach it from its origin or insertion and reattach it somewhere else on the bone.

Improving the flexibility of a client's muscles, such as the hamstrings, has long been a focus of many successful personal trainers. The thinking was, and still is, that by stretching the muscles in static positions (and even by utilizing some variation of proprioceptive neuromuscular facilitation), you can lengthen the fibers and release tension from the tissue.

In theory, this sounds great. However, detailed studies have shown that stretching, especially static holds, does little to release tension and improve movement and mobility in most populations. In fact, stretching prior to intense exercise could lead to an increase in injury risk from manipulating the length-tension relationship of the muscle.

Stretching can still have its place in certain programs though, as many aging clients benefit from flexibility training.

November 2nd

Lifting heavy weights does not necessarily coincide with muscle growth, specifically the "bulk" that many individuals fear. Resistance training can strengthen bones, increase muscle density, decrease body fat, and increase blood sugar utilization, but without added caloric intake and specific training protocols, hypertrophy on noticeable levels will not occur.

Men and women alike have expressed genuine fear at the possibility that resistance training would make them "bulky." Often, women express fear that they'll lose their feminine figure, while men assume they'll look like the guys on the covers of muscle magazines.

To the contrary, resistance exercise alone cannot increase someone's muscle mass to the point that they'd "lose their figure" or "look like they do steroids." To achieve these things, someone must consume calories in a surplus to increase their chance at muscular hypertrophy.

It's important to teach your clients about all the benefits of resistance training. Explain that muscle growth is only one benefit of resistance training, and one that takes additional efforts to truly realize.

November 3rd

Strength training is appropriate for everyone. The key is to adjust the intensity to meet the needs and capabilities of the client. No one, regardless of age, gender, physical condition, disease, or training experience should miss out on the benefits of a strength training plan.

Every population can benefit from implementing strength training into their programs.

The caveat with strength training is to adapt the intensity and complexity to meet the needs and capabilities of the individual performing it:

- Someone in their eighties should absolutely be strength training differently than an athlete in their early twenties.
- A fourteen-year-old teenager should be focusing on movement mastery instead of intensity, while a mid-thirties bodybuilder can focus on breaking down muscle tissue.

Strength training can improve nearly every aspect of a person's health and fitness, from bone density to sprinting speed. For this reason, it is safe to say that strength training is for everyone, so long as it is adapted to the needs of the person you are training.

November 4th

Functional training has become the hype word of the decade as many coaches abandon the traditional modes of exercise in favor of movements that apply to daily life. There is some truth here in the sense that training must account for the variety of movements that life can present. However, emphasizing functional exercises and abandoning the proven methods of the trade can often leave your clients without progress. Balance function with fitness and your clients will continually progress.

Functional training is an important effort that every trainer should undertake with every client they work with. Varied environments, exercising through the three planes of motion, and creating optimal movement patterns are ways of improving a client's function.

However, we must not go so far down the functional path that we no longer create a fitness effect with our clients. Spending too much time trying to increase the mobility at a specific joint, searching for "perfect" movement patterns, or enhancing someone's breathing patterns are all examples of being "too functional."

Balance your client's functional needs with the proven methods of improving your client's fitness.

November 5th

A personal trainer cannot treat or cure illnesses. Utilizing myofascial release, functional exercises, and even breathing drills will not "heal" someone. These tactics can greatly support lifestyle changes, a structured exercise routine, and the leadership of a doctor, physical therapist, or licensed massage therapist, but a trainer should not claim to heal or cure conditions.

One foul that far too many personal trainers commit is making the claim that they can "heal," "fix," or "cure" something. Such a claim isn't just incorrect in most cases—it's dangerous.

This is a blatant violation of our scope of practice as personal trainers, as there are ethical and legal ramifications to telling someone that you are capable of "curing" a disease or "fixing" a dysfunction.

Look closely at legal contracts that gyms provide to customers at point-of-sale and you'll see something like, "exercise is not intended to cure or treat any disease or known condition." This same type of notice is found on most supplements, massage contracts at a spa.

Avoid using these words in advertising and conversation and you'll be in the clear.

November 6th

*Low carbohydrate diets are not a cure-all for weight loss.
There is a lot of evidence, and more is found each day,
of their usefulness. However, reducing carbohydrate
intake is not a one-stop shop for losing body fat and
improving one's body composition. In fact, many people
end up gaining weight due to the increase in fat
consumption or the binge that follows avoidance. Always
start with improving lifestyle habits before cutting an
entire macronutrient out of someone's diet.*

If you only used the popular media as your source for nutrition information, then you'd likely come to believe that carbohydrates are the devil. It seems there's always a story about how avoiding carbohydrates is the real secret to weight loss.

These claims aren't baseless, of course. Lowering carbohydrate intake, especially in the form of simple sugars, starches, and grains, has been shown to lead to lower bodyweights in many people.

But it isn't that simple. Avoidance diets aren't easy to adhere to, causing many people to binge on whatever they've been cutting out when they slip up. Additionally, a reduction of carbohydrates can impact energy levels, which could upset someone's sleep schedule and drive to exercise daily.

November 7ᵗʰ

Protein is not a miracle calorie. Yes, it is a macronutrient that can help build muscle, contribute to burning fat, and keep you satiated for longer periods of time. However, it is not a macronutrient that should be abused and eaten in excess in the name of "avoiding carbohydrates" or "building more muscle." There is an upper threshold of what your body can handle.

Painted as "the perfect calorie," many people see no downside to increasing (and maximizing) their protein intake. In fact, many popular diets, such as keto and paleo, require high levels of protein intake.

Like most claims, this isn't completely crazy. There is some truth to the wonders of protein. It's metabolically active, does increase satiety, is needed to build muscle mass, and can contribute to increased fat loss.

Protein also has its downsides. Firstly, the human body can only absorb so much protein per hour.

Secondly, and most importantly, supercharging any macronutrient often leads to consuming too many calories per day, often causing unwanted weight gain.

Day by Day

November 8th

There is no one exercise that is so critical that it must occur in a client's program. Surely, all seven movement patterns should appear in a person's training protocol, but no specific exercise is so incredible that it can't be changed to something more suitable to the individual. Deadlifts are great, but not everyone can hinge in this way. Overhead pressing is great, but not everyone presents the shoulder mobility to do this.

In all areas of life, people invest too much energy arguing about who is right and who is wrong. One of those areas is fitness. In fact, it seems that the validity of a given exercise can be just as polarizing as politics or sports.

Take the deadlift, for example. There are legions of dedicated lifters, strength coaches, and academics who think the deadlift belongs in everyone's training program. Yet, there is an entire school of individuals—yoga instructors, performance coaches, and doctors—who feel the deadlift is an unnecessary risk.

We won't settle this debate here, but realize that the truth lies in the middle. Some people should deadlift, and others should not. Never marry yourself to a specific exercise and come to believe that it is one-size-fits-all. Few things in life are.

November 9th

Needing rest is not a sign of weakness or a lack of desire to push. Sure, some individuals are uncomfortable being uncomfortable and require a nudge to push themselves a bit harder, but most people have a positive relationship with the cells of their body and have a good idea of when they need to back it down and when they can ramp it up. Don't annihilate someone just because you can. Provide an enjoyable but challenging experience.

There has always been a subculture of fitness that thrives on annihilation. In recent years, the fringe has become the new normal. This can't continue.

The mentality that each workout should leave someone feeling exhausted, broken, and sore for days needs to be torn down. The idea that exercise is a punishment for bad dietary behavior needs to cease too.

These mindsets turn a blind eye toward the needs of each unique client. Some will respond well to these brutal challenges while most break down, lose motivation, and eventually fade back into inactivity.

Your job as a personal trainer isn't to crush people. Your job is to challenge your clients to get better each day without hurting their mind or body.

November 10th

High intensity interval training doesn't mean that you should push the gas pedal with no respect for the brake pedal. It seems the industry is bent on pushing people harder and giving them as little rest as possible. The peak work to rest ratio should be equal parts work and rest (1:1). Remember, high intensity is only high if there are other intensities too.

Trainers and exercise enthusiasts alike have become too obsessed with high-intensity workouts. There is always that person in a group exercise class who skips the mobility or core work to run in place instead. There is also that trainer who never relents with their clients, always pushing them to be out of breath.

These high intensity workouts can be great challenges for anyone, but they must be used intelligently. Going all out every time has consequences that include injury risk, metabolic disruption, and skewed perception of what constitutes "a good workout."

Be the trainer who utilizes HIIT workouts as a weekly challenge or as a supplement to a structured training program. Training requires balance between the extremes.

November 11th

Workouts of the day (WODs) are not an optimal way of improving one's fitness in the long term. While this popular modality catches the eye of Instagram followers and attendees of CrossFit boxes around the globe, it does not consider the individual needs for a person's progression over time. Always take the time to develop a specific program for the specific client in front of you.

As CrossFit grew in popularity, so too did the use of all-in-one daily workouts as a way of programming for personal trainers. This programming style (meant for small group training) became a crutch to avoid doing a lot of prep work before sessions.

Simply put, any personal trainer who generates a single workout for all their clients to do each day is lazy or incapable of doing more. While this may come off as brash or rude, it's important to remember the job title: *personal* trainer.

Each client should receive a personalized program that acknowledges their capabilities, needs, and history while pushing toward their goals and future. Anything less falls short of meeting the base requirement of the job description. Take the time to develop unique programs for all your clients.

November 12th

There is no modality that's better than another. Claiming that kettlebells are better than dumbbells is like saying that oranges are better than apples. Both have distinct purposes in a person's workout or diet. Some people will prefer one over the other and that is perfectly fine; however, a personal preference is not a rule. Avoid coaching as though one modality were superior.

At the end of the day, no piece of exercise equipment has ever gotten someone fit. Rather, a person has gotten themselves fit by giving a lot of effort and working their tail off utilizing said exercise equipment.

Someone could lose body fat with barbells, kettlebells or dumbbells. They could build muscle too.

For that reason, it is important to never claim that one piece of equipment is better than another.

Sure, a barbell is better for training maximum load lifts and kettlebells are better for dynamic unilateral movements. But barbells can't stimulate a unilateral challenge and many clients do not like the feeling of kettlebells.

Everything has its strengths and weaknesses.

November 13th

Increasing cardiovascular exercise is not going to contribute to significant body mass loss if caloric intake is kept too high. If your client is increasing their mileage, then you must coach them to decrease their caloric intake. Just the same, if your client is afraid of doing too much cardiovascular exercise and losing their hard-earned muscle mass, then increase their carbohydrate intake to balance the scales.

The myth of cardiovascular exercise ruining someone's muscularity or strength has caused a lot of men, young and old, to avoid a training modality that could do wonders for their hearts.

The fear is that the caloric expenditure of cardiovascular exercise, say running, could cause a person to burn muscle mass as fuel. This catabolism would ruin any efforts they are making to build impressive muscle.

This fear is baseless so long as a person isn't running long distances on a regular basis (above ten miles) and is consuming enough calories in their diet to offset the expenditure.

Your clients should be doing at least sixty minutes of cardiovascular exercise a week.

November 14ᵗʰ

Cardiovascular exercise is less about the fat-burning, calorie-torching sweat fests that most people envision it to be and more about increasing the heart and ventilatory rates, mobilizing nutrients and hormones in the blood, and providing an uptick of oxygen to tissues throughout the body.

Continuing with yesterday's topic of cardiovascular exercise and myth busting, doing cardio is about so much more than simply burning calories.

For most, a bout of cardiovascular exercise is the necessary evil for their weight loss efforts. Not unsurprisingly, many individuals who only use cardio training never quite achieve their ideal physique.

The real benefit of cardiovascular exercise extends well beyond fat loss and weight management. The list of health factors that are improved include:

- Lower resting heart rate
- Lower blood sugar
- Increased levels of dopamine
- Increased metabolic activity

Your clients should be reaping these benefits.

November 15th

*There is no limit to how frequently you can train your
body. In fact, you and your clients should exercise every
single day. The key, though, is to manage the intensity
and variety of the routine. Finding a balance between
strength training, cardio, and restorative practices such
as Pilates and yoga will lead to long-term success.*

Contrary to popular belief, no one needs a rest day.
In fact, there is a lot of data to support the idea that
exercising daily is one of the keys to a longer, healthier
life.

The key to accepting this tip is reframing your perspective
of what constitutes "exercise." In modern culture, only
the high intensity sessions that leave us sore and sweaty
seem to be counted. Really, anything that elevates the
heart rate for at least twenty minutes while the body
moves through space is exercise.

A long walk on the beach, a quick yoga flow, or a two-
mile jog count as exercise.

Coach your clients to move for at least twenty minutes
a day, every day, and you'll be amazed at how much
progress they are able to make with other aspects of
their fitness program.

November 16th

Fitness should not supersede wellness. At no point should a client's ability to do a heavy lift, run a competitive mile, or look a certain way overtake their ability to be healthy. Eating disorders, body dysmorphia, and a host of other psychological issues have been caused by coaches who only cared about results.

Many competitive physique athletes, bodybuilders, powerlifters, marathon runners, models, and CrossFit athletes look like pure fitness. One look and you can't help but be impressed.

But their bodies are not actually healthy. Dramatic dieting techniques, supplements, and exhausting exercise programs wear down their hearts, livers, and digestive systems.

Many incredibly fit people struggle with sleep, digestion, body image, anxiety, and depression.

The key is to coach yourself and your clients to push their physical fitness while still respecting the other aspects of their health. There is no sense getting to single digit body fat only to have a heart attack once you get there.

Never sacrifice health for fitness goals. Find a way to make them work together.

November 17th

A trainer does not have to look like the fitness models on the covers of magazines to be good at their job. Remember that what you look like doesn't reflect your ability to listen, coach, and improve someone else. You should be able to do most of the things that you prescribe, but you don't need to be eye candy to be a great coach. Just the same, don't assume your physique is indicative of your skills as a coach—many fit people make horrible trainers.

If you only look at social media or popular magazines, you'll think that being extraordinarily fit is a prerequisite for being a great trainer.

Sure, being able to take care of yourself demonstrates that you can train hard and eat well. It shows that you know what you are doing, at least for yourself.

Being in spectacular shape doesn't qualify you to coach others or to solve the complex issues that may face your clients. In fact, many highly fit people have difficulty relating to the struggles their clients face, presenting a barrier to coaching.

Some of the best coaches in the world train hard and eat well, but their biggest priority isn't their body, it's their clients.

November 18ᵗʰ

What you can do in a gym should have no impact on what you ask you ask of your clients. Your Instagram videos, performance at the weekend powerlifting meet, or mega box jump should not impact what your clients are doing. Many trainers will push their way of doing things on their clients, and this shouldn't happen. A client's goals should dictate the program over your own.

Many trainers have their clients replicate their own workouts. Their thought process is, "I can do it and it gets/keeps me fit, so you should try it too."

This couldn't be more off-base. As trainers, we are often significantly more fit than our client base. We have a better understanding of how our body should move, what we should feel, and why we are doing what we do.

For this reason, we must always think twice before having our clients "do what we do."

An extension of this includes our bias for particular training modalities. Having a passion for something is great, but you must always ask yourself if your client will redeem benefits from your style of training.

November 19th

*Eating six meals a day is no better than three meals, or
two, or twelve. The key is to coach your clients to find
sustainable eating patterns that can persist over time.
Remember that no single plan is better than another.
People have found success with varying numbers of
meals. Find what works and stick to it.*

One of the most common dietary strategies that trainers
recommend is increasing the number of meals a client
eats per day.

This recommendation makes sense if you consider that
eating smaller meals more frequently can limit caloric
consumption, increase metabolic efficiency, and help
block snacking habits.

However, many clients don't have the means or time
to prepare so many small meals, won't adhere to meal
prepping, or will struggle to eat so frequently without
feeling sick.

For this reason, we say that eating a certain number
of meals is not as important as eating nutrient-dense
foods in the right amounts each day. Whether a client
eats their necessary vegetables and protein in six meals
or three meals matters less than that they consume the
right nutrients.

November 20th

Supplements, especially those from multi-level marketing schemes, are not necessary for your client's success. Do not fall for the allure of a phone salesman promising you money, success, and better client retention just because you sell their brand of pills and powders. You are a better coach for resisting these ploys.

It can be tempting to take, recommend, or even sell supplements. Your job is to get results, right?

Supplements are not the missing link. Most supplements are under-dosed, under-researched, and often useless. Many of the ingredients that are studied don't work in pill or powder form or require significantly higher doses to be effective.

For this reason, avoid recommending supplements to your clients. This even includes multi-vitamins and fish oils: two "safe" supplements that don't have favorable research either.

Your best bet is to focus on providing the best training service you can while coaching your clients to eat the right things. This is what's proven to get results.

November 21st

Not all calories are created equal. Contrary to the idea that any calorie that fits into your daily allotment is OK, junk foods lack vitamins and minerals that are necessary for your client's success. "If it fits your macros" sounds great on a T-shirt and as a hashtag on social media, but your clients need to focus on nutrition-rich food first.

A few years back, a diet known as "if it fits your macros" took the main stage. The argument was simple:

If you eat at or under your maintenance calories each day while honoring your ideal macronutrient breakdowns, then you can "snack" on anything you want. Donuts would be considered healthy carbohydrates and fats if you hit your target numbers.

This is ludicrous diet advice for anyone who isn't a refined dieter with a challenging training regimen. For the average person, this advice doesn't highlight the importance of nutrient density (vitamins and minerals).

Most people need to eat more vegetables and fruits and less junk. Telling them they can eat any carbohydrate or fat is risky business and often fails.

November 22nd

Running on the treadmill is not the same as flat ground running. Many people consider the miles the same when tracking a client's cardiovascular workload. But, there is much more effort set forth when running on flat ground. The strides must propel you forward instead of up and down like on a treadmill. This changes the mechanics, the metabolic effort, and where stress is placed on the body.

Let's start this tip off by acknowledging that running on a treadmill is just fine. It is a great way to get your mileage in, knock out some sprints, or walk at an incline.

However, a treadmill does not replace running outdoors for those who are looking to improve their stride quality.

Running on a belt that moves underneath them could not be more different than foot strikes on pavement, which they must push against. Each stride on a treadmill is straight up and down whereas outdoor running requires a forward lean and projection from the feet.

Running outdoors is also much more challenging than a treadmill since the person is actively moving their body forward and navigating terrain.

November 23rd

Sore lower backs are not just a symptom of being weak and undertrained. Often, underactive glutes, lats, and core musculature cause the lower back to inflame. These underactive muscles, when paired with poor thoracic mobility and the inability to separate the lumbar spine from the hips in movement patterns, leads to lower back issues. Always look around the source of the discomfort for the real causes of the pain.

Lower back pain has a myriad of causes that range from injuries to poor posture, caused by underactive musculature.

It's important to first acknowledge that a personal trainer's job is not to diagnose or treat pain. Any time a client reports notable pain, it's critical to refer out to physical therapists and doctors. These cases are beyond a trainer's scope of practice.

However, low-level, chronic discomfort can often be remediated by emphasizing glute, abductor, hamstring, core, and lat strength. All of these areas are critical load-bearing muscles of the body and can eliminate the amount of work that lower back extensors must do.

November 24th

While bench pressing is often the prescription for a bigger chest, it's actually an increase in pulling exercises, such as rows and pullups, that works best. As the scapulae retract and depress, thoracic extension increases, which pushes the chest forward and upward, creating a bigger surface area. In terms of training the chest, emphasize dumbbells and the incline angle to increase the cross-sectional area of the pectorals.

Ask most people what you do to build a bigger chest and you'll hear some variation of "bench press." This answer isn't wrong, but it isn't completely right either.

Many guys walk around with internally rotated shoulders, elevated and protracted scapulae, and weak core muscles. A training program that increases pulling exercises (retraction and depression) while strengthening the core (lifting the ribs) can improve the size of someone's chest by addressing their posture.

When training the chest, slower repetitions with dumbbells and an incline angle has been shown to increase pectoral breakdown, a key to muscle growth.

November 25th

Doing more exercise and eating fewer calories is not the best prescription for weight loss, especially for those who have a lot of weight to lose. It's better to emphasize mastery of one domain at a time. First, increase exercise frequency and quality. Then, begin changing what is consumed in someone's diet. Last, begin adjusting total caloric intake.

Most people assume that in order to get in shape, they must exercise more and eat less. This thought process isn't completely off-base, but it isn't right either.

The safest bet for someone, especially someone who needs to lose weight, is to increase their exercise first. This is because they will need additional fuel to power their workouts, which will seem like a shock to their system.

After the client has become adjusted to increased energy expenditure, you can begin lowering their caloric intake. A slow "elevator" approach is the best way to ensure a client doesn't damage their metabolism or cause stagnation.

Alternating between increased energy expenditure and lower caloric intake is the best and safest method to help a client lose weight and keep it off.

November 26th

*Eating late at night isn't bad if you aren't one for eating
in the morning. Eating in the morning isn't bad if you
don't like eating late at night. Eating at both ends of the
day, however, is usually not best. Coach your clients to
eat within the time intervals that work best for their life
and not based on a random factoid found online.*

Eating late at night has become the worst thing you
can do in the eyes of many internet health bloggers and
personal trainers.

Eating cookies and snack foods certainly isn't good.

However, some people don't like eating in the mornings,
practice intermittent fasting, or have trouble getting
their calories in throughout the day due to scheduling.

For these people, a late-night meal may help them achieve
their goals. Consistently undereating can stagnate
metabolism by causing the body to protect fat stores
and lower the basal metabolic rate.

Listen to your clients and learn about their schedules.
They should eat when it works best for them, so long as
they are eating foods that help them move toward their
goals and not using the time as an excuse to eat junk
food.

November 27th

Being a great business person and selling a fair amount of sessions and maintaining a full book of clients doesn't make you a great trainer. That requires being there for your clients as people while putting their individual qualities first as you program and train. Success is measured by the quality of your work and not the quantity of your clientele.

It matters to be able to differentiate financial success from the quality of your work. In every industry, there are individuals who make far more money than others even when their skill sets are of significantly lower quality.

In personal training, everyone assumes that a busy trainer is a great trainer. Clearly, their schedule is full, their clients keep showing up, and their bills are paid. They may have thousands of social media followers and even get paid to advertise certain products.

But ask yourself, do any of these things represent their ability to coach, care, and create lasting results for their clients? Are they using the right science, correcting form appropriately, and conducting their sessions with full focus on the person who is paying them?

November 28th

There is a stigma against trainers who work at commercial gyms. It's as though you can't be taken seriously unless you are willing to go into debt and open your own location. This couldn't be more incorrect. There are many great trainers who are employed by various commercial brands throughout the world. Some people just don't want, or aren't ready for, the hassles that come with owning your own business. This doesn't change their value as coaches.

For some reason, working in a commercial gym isn't respected by industry veterans in the manner that it should be. It's as if working for someone else is indicative of your skill set.

They are viewed as less skilled than those individuals who have taken the leap and started their own business. We must be very clear:

Sure, some trainers don't do the best job at these gyms, it's a numbers game. However, there are superstars out there and they deserve respect and the opportunity to be noticed too.

Some people are scared to take on the risk of owning their own business while others just don't want the stress. It's important to judge trainers by how they train and not where they work.

November 29th

The best trainers don't have to tell their clientele how great
they are, undercut their competitors, or market their services
in dubious ways. Doing these things doesn't make you a
savvy business person; it means you're worried that your
service isn't enough to keep people coming back. The best
coaches don't need to compete against others or toot their
own horn. They simply show up and deliver an amazing
service and let their clients do the talking. When it does come
to their marketing plan? They focus on what they've done
(and can prove) instead of what they "could" do.

This tip is very simple. The best coaches in the world don't need to yell from the rooftops about their skills, nor do they need to do shady things to get business.

They simply show up to work and deliver outstanding customer service and training every day. They study on their own time and work side-by-side with other professionals to move the industry forward.

Position yourself in your market as a great professional, a talented trainer, and an incredible person. There is enough business available for everyone who does their job well to make good money.

November 30th

You don't need a college education to be a great trainer. It never hurts to be formally educated, but this field does not require it. If you are a diligent student who seeks knowledge from all sources, a critical thinker who knows better than to chase the shiny object, and a good person who truly cares, then you can have an amazing career.

The value of a college degree in the field of personal training is an often-debated topic. On the one hand, a college degree provides someone a wonderful knowledge base on which to build the rest of their career. On the other hand, you can learn a lot of what you learn in a degree program elsewhere.

Whether you have a degree or not, what matters is your continued dedication to learning your craft, challenging your beliefs, and expanding your mind. Your education doesn't have to be formal—it just needs to happen.

From there, great trainers use their education to develop programs that deliver results, while their personality and thoughtfulness deliver an experience that makes clients feel welcome and successful.

Do it how you want. Just be a proactive student.

December

Taking Care of Yourself

"December used to be very difficult for me. For many years, I fought the transition to the new year, was generally exhausted at the end of the year, and just wanted to hide."

—Brad Feld

"Just taking care of yourself is a job of its own."

—Joanna Krupa

December 1st

From the outside looking in, the fitness industry seems like a whole lot of fun. Gym clothing is work attire and you get to "exercise" and "socialize" all day. Sure, these things are true. But anyone who has worked a few years in the industry knows that the jewel shines brighter from far away. Acknowledging the challenges of your profession, no matter how far along the career curve you are, is the first step to taking care of yourself.

Many people become personal trainers because they get excited at the idea of marrying their hobby with a career that pays them well for their time. It isn't that easy.

It is important to remember that a lot of trainers never truly become "full-time." Whether it's a lack of clients or other responsibilities, many people never achieve the financial freedom they thought they would.

The hours are tough. Early mornings and late nights are necessary in an industry that works while other people are off.

Dealing with people all day has its stress too. Someone people aren't easy to work with. You must be OK with the variations in human personalities.

December 2nd

Clients will bring their drama to you. This is normal, and it is completely normal to help them sort it out while they train with you. However, you need to have your own way of dumping this emotional weight before leaving for the day. You don't want to wear the problems of your clients at home.

One of the risks of working directly with people is that their issues can quickly become your issues. Whether you are a doctor, a therapist, a personal trainer, or even a bartender, people will use you as their sounding board.

You want to be there for your clients emotionally as best as you can. Usually, the best bet is to simply listen and nod as they tell you everything they feel compelled to reveal. Occasionally you'll provide advice, but always be mindful of your role. Never act as someone's therapist.

Concerning you though, it's important for you to be able to separate yourself from whatever your client may bring as you soon as the session ends. Your job is to deliver the best fitness product possible. This requires you to try your best to leave emotional weight behind you after tough sessions.

December 3rd

Remember that everyone in this life has good days and bad days. Sometimes a client can be a real jerk and it can sting. Don't take a bad attitude personally, and look to be the bright spot in this person's day. Some people, though, can't be helped and you'll need to decide if this person's money is worth your sanity.

Sometimes your clients can be real jerks. They'll bring in whatever emotional baggage they're carrying and turn it into vitriol and contempt for you and your practice.

Other times, you'll encounter clients who talk down to you or treat you as though you were an employee of theirs. In both scenarios, two things need to happen:

1. A discussion about the respect you expect and deserve must take place, and
2. You'll have to examine your relationship with them and ask yourself if this is a pattern of behavior or an isolated incident.

If a person consistently takes out their bad days on you or regularly disrespects you and your profession, then you may want to part ways with that client. The rest of the time, you need to take a deep breath and forgive them.

December 4th

Never fear losing a client due to a lack of social connection. You both want to enjoy a training session. You may have the skillset they need, but their adherence to you, or your patience for them, is tested because you don't mesh. Be the best professional by setting them up with their next trainer and maintain contact over time.

Like any relationship in life, sometimes it just doesn't work. Personal training requires a certain level of socialization and connection for it to be successful.

You don't need to become best friends, of course, but you should be able spend an hour together without being annoyed by the other person's presence.

While it may be hard to walk away from money by setting a client up with another trainer, you could benefit greatly in the long term.

Put simply, both people involved will be happier in the long run. You will have less stress and strife at work and they'll work with someone they get along with.

This is just one more reason why it's important to maintain great relationships with other trainers in your market.

December 5th

It's easy to let your clients run your schedule, especially when you are just beginning your career or starting over. You want clients, any clients, to fill your schedule and help you make personal training profitable. If you compromise too much, you'll never get that time back. Set time in your schedule that is off limits.

In the early days of a trainer's career, any client is a good client. Your schedule is open, and you're eager to build a business and brand.

It can be tempting to say yes to anything, and anyone, as you try to fill up your schedule. However, it is still important to take care of yourself and box out hours that are for you and your own health.

Once you become busier, you'll find that it's much harder to keep up with your own fitness, to find a comfortable time to eat a meal, and to have a personal life. So, avoid having to cut down your business by preparing your schedule while you still can.

Lastly, know that it's OK to say no to clients. They'll ask about training on a day that you planned to have off, or they'll want to switch to an inconvenient time.

December 6th

Avoid training every single day of the week. It's OK if you want to train a few sessions six days a week, or a lot of sessions five days a week, or whatever you dream up. What should be avoided though, is having clients every single day and not being able to enjoy freedom from your fitness facility.

Building off yesterday's tip about managing your schedule from the get-go, it's equally as important to schedule yourself time away from the facility.

Working every day as a personal trainer isn't as simple as just showing up and doing your job. You have to consider your commute, the time it takes to get ready, and the high probability that'll you spend longer at the gym than you intended.

It's important to push yourself to work hard and it's important to be available for your clients. There is a certain level of martyrdom that is required to be a successful trainer, no doubt. That being said, you need to set boundaries and respect them.

Yes, even you can disrespect your own boundaries. Don't jeopardize your long-term success in favor of short-term gain.

December 7th

Aim to be as authentic to yourself as you can be. It's common for personal trainers to mirror their clients to appease them and seem stimulating, however, being yourself is one of the best ways to ensure your business is consistent and effective. More importantly, putting on a "mask" just to get through the day is exhausting and can contribute to issues down the line.

The fitness industry is full of people who are wearing masks. Afraid to be the real version of themselves, many trainers create personas that they think clients want. Instead of being true to who they really are, they morph into an unhealthy person: someone full of ego, narcissism, and fear.

From day one, be true to yourself. Authenticity is all too rare in the world, and especially in the fitness industry. Be honest about your accomplishments, open about your shortcomings, and level-headed with your expectations.

Doing the opposite puts you at risk of true failure down the road. True failure is when your world shatters around you because everything you've ever built was built upon lies and bravado. Avoid this catastrophe by being willing to be the real you in front of the world.

December 8th

Social media can make you believe that the only great trainers in the industry have razor sharp six packs, perfect tans, and hair that never falls out of place. This is false. Don't let outward pressures make you question your effectiveness with your clients.

Social media is mostly good for the world. However, its downsides are exceptionally dangerous.

Fitness is one of the most popular subjects on social media channels. Every single day, trainers and fitness enthusiasts alike are posting selfies of their incredible bodies followed by some series of words that make them sound poetic and thoughtful.

Some are, but many are merely creating a fitness personality that they think attracts clients.

Be conscious of who you are and what you offer the world. You may not have the best abs or the biggest deadlift, but you provide tremendous value every day.

Let your clients and your happiness be the judge of your success as a personal trainer. Don't measure yourself against people who aren't even real.

December 9th

*Personal training naturally attracts alpha personalities,
thus breeding an environment of competition and stress.
Assess your tolerance for competition and indulge in it
only as much as you can handle. Don't worry about
what another trainer can lift or how many blog posts
another person publishes each week. Instead, focus on
how you can get a little better every day.*

Your work environment, and that includes the internet, is full of personalities who are competitive, aggressive, and even narcissistic. Most personal trainers are alpha personalities.

They want to lead. They crave attention and responsibility. And they want to stand out from their peers.

This probably sounds just like you.

Just remember that the only thing you can control is yourself. If someone writes an incredible article, then that is on them. If someone shares an incredible photo of their body on the beach, then that is their choice.

Control your career and your happiness by focusing on delivering outstanding sessions, being a great person, and by challenging yourself to grow into a better version of yourself.

December 10th

You need to exercise. No matter how busy you get, there needs to be an effort on your part to stay active. You don't need to look like a model, lift a small truck, or run an elite time in a marathon, but you need to present yourself as a person who practices what you preach.

As a personal trainer, you know the benefits of exercise better than most. For that reason, there is absolutely no excuse (beyond medical conditions and injuries) for you to skip out on your own fitness.

This doesn't mean that you need to be setting power-lifting records, running marathons, or looking like a fitness model. But it does mean you should be challenging yourself in every aspect of your own fitness.

For one, you should be the type of person who practices what you preach. Secondly, you should understand how every type of exercise feels so that you can provide better empathy and understanding for your clients.

Lastly, your job is hard. The hours are long, and the stress is high, which is exactly why you must train your body.

Taking care of your fitness should be a priority.

December 11th

Schedule your workout time the same way you schedule clients. Do not negotiate this time unless you can find another untouchable spot to replace it. It's important for your sanity and your passion to maintain your own fitness routine.

It's painfully easy to let your day get away from you when you are a personal trainer. It's equally as easy to forego your workout in favor of sleep, food, or anything that isn't inside the walls of your gym.

For these reasons, it's important that you schedule your workouts the same way you schedule your training sessions, meetings, and business management. This will help keep you accountable to yourself and your fitness plan even when everything in your life is fighting against you.

Sometimes your clients are going to want to jump into these times in your schedule. Obviously, you have bills to pay, but be cautious with giving up your personal time in favor of making a few more dollars.

Remember, your own fitness matters too. Your business, your health, and your family need you to take care of yourself.

December 12th

Surround yourself with fitness professionals who are actively trying to get better. Join them on the journey to becoming a better student of the body and its functions. Attend conferences, read blogs and studies, and have long discussions whenever possible to harness the power of your creative brain and the potency of conviction in what you believe.

It is really easy to become friends with people who share similar interests with you. Maybe you love to watch basketball or you're both fans of superhero movies.

But sometimes our relationships don't make us better. When becoming friends with other trainers, it's important that you ask yourself if they make you better in some way. This doesn't mean you should only be friends with successful personal trainers though. It means that you should ask yourself if these people share similar work ethic, optimism, and dreams as you.

One of the best ways to meet other trainers like yourself is to attend conferences, get continuing education credits, and interact on the internet. You are the average of the five people you associate yourself with most, so ask yourself, who are you?

December 13th

Whether you work at a commercial facility or you run your own business, there are financial and performance goals you need to set and meet. This pressure is unfortunately inescapable unless you win the lottery and choose to train as a hobby. Know the numbers you need to hit and create systems that help you run your business and hit those markers.

No matter which way you cut it, a career in personal training is still a business. This means that you'll always have sales goals, marketing needs, and require a bit of business acumen.

Trainers at commercial gyms usually must meet goals set for them by managers and corporate leaders. These goals can be stressful and hard to meet, but it's important to remember that you can do so if you simplify your process and focus on being a great trainer who is present at the gym consistently.

Trainers who run their own business have much more to consider, so the advice for them isn't so simple. However, running a "lean" business and delivering great results can turn your clients into your marketing department. Discover the magic number of clients that your business needs.

December 14th

*Be sure to get time outside in the sun whenever you can.
Too much time indoors has been shown to increase the
occurrence of depression and can spoil your motivations. It's
ironic that a career that emphasizes health often places its
workers under artificial lighting for extended periods of time.*

There are legitimate health benefits to sunlight exposure. From releasing vitamin D to fighting anxiety and depression, the sun can improve our health.

Unfortunately, so many trainers miss out on the sun because they are spending their time inside of their fitness facility rendering sessions and running their business.

Taking care of yourself requires getting outdoors whenever you can. Go on a run, do yoga in the park, or simply lie down and work on your tan while reading a book. It matters less *what* you do and much more *where* you are doing it.

If you live in less sunny places, then you may want to invest in a SAD lamp: a specially designed bulb that simulates the amount of UV that is found in sunlight. While it isn't as good as the real thing, it's still better than spending no time in the sun.

December 15th

Take breaks when your clients do. It is not uncommon to have slow July and August productivity in the training industry. Use this time for yourself to get away from the gym and take a vacation, dive into your education, or enjoy some evenings at home with friends and family.

Personal training has a bit of an ebb and flow to it.

The first few months of the year bring an increase in business as a new year inspires people everywhere to try at their fitness again. This rush tends to wear off as March comes along, but soon enough the promise of warm weather inspires people to try to get "beach ready."

The summer brings slower business as people travel and spend more time outdoors. The fall brings another rush of traffic before the holiday season turns gyms into ghost towns.

This pattern repeats itself. It's important to structure your own time off around these breaks. This will help you maximize your earnings while still allowing yourself time for vacation and relaxation.

Plan your finances too by saving money while you are busy. Build your buffer.

December 16th

Keep strong relationships with your non-fitness friends.
Not everyone in this world wakes and squats or substitutes
vegetables for fries at every meal. It's healthy to be
around those who may take fitness less seriously. It
will remind you that fitness is indeed a lifestyle but one
that doesn't define you as a person.

The lifestyle of a personal trainer can make it hard to keep healthy relationships with anyone who isn't a personal trainer.

Your work schedule has you getting up early and your evening schedule makes happy hours and dinner reservations hard to attend.

Missing these events can leave you in the fitness vacuum for too long. Not enjoying the occasional night out or cheat meal can make it hard for you to be empathetic with your clients, a key to success.

Not everyone in the world loves exercise and healthy food like you. These are the people who are going to hire you, so it's important to understand their lifestyle and respect their choices.

Lastly, it can be refreshing to your spirit to spend time with people who don't want to debate the attributes of the deadlift. Your brain will thank you.

December 17th

Read both fiction and non-fiction. While fitness books, business books, and the entire self-help industry can help you become a more successful fitness professional, it's the fiction that takes your mind on a journey and gifts you true creativity. It may seem crazy at first that Hemmingway could improve your business, but stories are our best teachers.

Too many adults stop reading fiction at a certain point in their career and it severely damages their ability to be their best self.

While non-fiction books about training, business, and psychology can help you apply new tactics and grow your brand, it's the journey fiction takes you on that makes leaps possible.

Stories increase your creativity and enhance your ability to think outside of the box. It can be hard to imagine that F. Scott Fitzgerald could help you make more money, but once you begin reading his work, you might soon find yourself having creative solutions to old problems.

Storytelling is also the most effective method of teaching. Reading fiction can help you better tell the story of fitness to your clients and other coaches.

December 18th

Keep a daily thought journal. You don't need to confess your love to your crush, but you do need to confess things to yourself. Exploring your day with the intent of fitting the entire happening into a few sentences can help you organize your life effectively. Plus, when you succeed at your endeavors, you can look back and track your journey.

The human mind is an advanced machine. However, it often fails at remembering little details, documenting emotions, and keeping track of those ideas that feel like magic.

Avoid forgetting the things that are important by taking a few moments each day to journal. It doesn't have to be profound, but it should highlight the big events of the day or any striking thoughts you might be having.

Writing about your life is a tremendous way to better understand it. Sometimes you can't think of an answer when the problem is in your head, but you immediately find a solution once you read the problem with your eyes.

This level of disassociation allows you to view your life from a distance, which is key to maintaining a level-headed approach to your life and business.

December 19th

Appreciate things. Appreciate people. Appreciate the world. In the rat race, it can be easy to forget about what you are already enjoying. You could be having a coffee with your partner looking out over the rolling countryside of Italy and still your mind wanders to the happenings of another trainer, celebrity, or your bills. Enjoy something every morning and every night by appreciating it verbally.

We keep our head down too much.

It's been ingrained in us that the only way to be successful is to forego simple pleasures and only work until you get to your goals.

Many "success" coaches preach the idea of purposely skipping out on pleasurable experiences until you deserve them and have earned the right to enjoy them.

They are wrong and only say that now because they want to make their own story sound harder than it was. Chances are, they stopped and smelled the roses too.

Take a breath each day and enjoy the world you live in, the people you know, and the feeling of being alive. You weren't born to work and die. You are here to experience all that life has to offer.

December 20th

Get your rest whenever you can. Personal training is a career with early mornings and late nights. It's not uncommon to have large gaps of time in the middle of your day when you become a busy personal trainer. This is a great time to exercise, work on your side projects, or simply take a nap. There is nothing wrong with hitting reset at 2pm on a Tuesday if you need it.

One of the greatest gifts of a personal training career is the ability to create your own schedule. It allows you to create blocks of time for personal needs, workouts, or an amazing mid-day nap.

Utilize the times you have off to rest. Your job requires you to be on your feet for hours on end. Your own workouts beat up your body and the early hour at which you wake up can make 2pm feel like 6pm.

When you get those breaks in the middle of your day, use them to take naps, watch movies, read books, or lie on your couch and breathe. You can also use this time to write blogs, work on side projects, and cultivate the life that you dream of.

The hours of a personal trainer are tough, but if you create a plan and stick to it, you can get more done in a day than can most people you know.

December 21st

*Balance your private time with your necessary sleep.
If you've spent the whole evening at the gym, it can
be tempting to stay up a little later and have some personal
space to watch your favorite show, play some games,
read a book, or just sit with your thoughts. Do these
things, but always be mindful of your wake-up time.
Don't make morning-you despise night-you.*

Coming home late at night is an extremely common occurrence for a personal trainer. It could easily be 8 or 9pm after a nighttime run of three or four clients.

When you get home, especially when you are younger, you might want to stay up later and watch a movie or play some games to blow off some steam. You might want to grab a drink with a friend or go on a date.

You should absolutely do these things.

However, make sure that you also get your sleep. Anything less than six hours per night causes major detriment to your health and performance. Getting about eight hours is most optimal, but life doesn't always make that possible.

Whether it's a Tuesday or a Friday, do your best to get to bed at a reasonable hour and allow your mind and body the chance to recover.

December 22nd

*Have hobbies that have absolutely nothing to do with
movement or fitness and enjoy leisure activities that
don't involve breaking a sweat. As trainers, we spend all
day on our feet, challenge our body with our own workouts,
and often engage in weekend sporting activities for fun. This
is all fine, but you should also have hobbies that
involve sitting right on your tailbone and enjoying
cerebral stimulation.*

Ask yourself this question:

*When was the last time you had fun doing something that
didn't involve fitness or movement?*

For many personal trainers, there is a long pause and a
hesitancy, because everything they do is physical.

First and foremost, know that you should be proud of
yourself and never change your ways. People who stay
in motion tend to live longer, healthier lives.

However, realize that your body will thank you for
some rest. Reading a book, playing games, or putting
together puzzles are all wonderful leisure activities.
Sure, your body isn't moving, but your brain will be
working hard to process information.

December 23rd

Extend your own workouts to places where you don't work. You may know of a competing location down the road that has reasonably priced guest passes, so go there sometimes. Eventually, your passion becomes work and the sanctuary you call home starts to grow old and tired. This is normal, so have backup plans for your workout that don't involve you being at work.

This message applies mostly to personal trainers who work at commercial gyms, but everyone who has a home base can relate.

We often spend too much time in the gym we work out of. Between our work schedules and our own fitness routines, we can grow unhappy and feel stale whenever we are there.

This is because you get tired of your surroundings. The gym soon feels no different than an office: a place to do work and have minimal fun. Your own workouts even get intruded on by clients and co-workers who want your attention.

Break up the monotony by working out outside, working out at other gyms, and doing things in your home. Keep yourself fresh.

December 24th

Limit your email correspondence to hours that you'd see clients. There is nothing wrong with telling your clients, "Hey, I don't answer emails after 10pm or before 6am." Respect your peace and create a business that reflects this.

The presence of email on our phones makes running our businesses much easier. We can answer our clients and expand our business from anywhere in the world.

However, many clients and leads see this as an open invitation to communicate with you at all times of the day. This can make a client feel like it's OK to email you and expect responses in the middle of the night or to communicate with you multiple times a day.

Be sure to outline your policies with clients early on in your relationship to ensure that they know that you have boundaries too.

Quiet time between 10pm and 6am is a great place to start, but feel free to make additional requests, such as no more than one email per day or that emails be formatted in bullet points.

You are a person before you are a personal trainer.

December 25th

Develop deeper conversations with your clients. You don't need to force a friendship or spend time together outside of the gym with those who pay you for your services, but it can benefit you to ask questions about them and their lives. Coffee with a client who has a story to tell could change your life forever.

Everyone has a story to tell. More importantly, everyone holds a life lesson within them that could help someone else immensely if it were shared.

Your clients are people who have had success and failures, good and bad, happy and sad. Many will have stories to tell about how they got to you, why they need you, and other important elements of their lives.

As you continue to train them for extended periods of time (think years), you'll want to have deeper conversations that unlock these stories. Connecting on a more human level can elevate both of your lives at the same time.

Your client will feel heard and you might just learn a thing or two. Each of your clients has stories of their own and could provide insights and connections that may help you too.

December 26th

Stay close to those who helped get you where you are. It's easy to put your head down and grind away the sessions, day after day, year after year. But time passes, and people eventually feel hurt when we no longer turn around and give them thanks and love. Your parents, caretakers, friends, and mentors are all people who deserve your time.

No one gets to the top of a mountain alone. Even the world's best climbers have Sherpas and guides who help get them there.

In your career, you've likely had many people, from family and friends to perfect strangers, help you get to where you are.

As you continue to succeed and progress in your life, be sure to turn around and give those people their due love. Thank them whenever you can for whatever they've done. Look for ways that you can give back to them too.

Sometimes, you are given the opportunity to help someone who once helped you—a tremendously powerful experience when it happens. As you evolve and grow, look for opportunities to do just that and you'll find yourself as the centerpiece of an incredible social network.

December 27th

Find a mentor, be someone's mentor, and be amongst a community of similarly skilled individuals. By having someone illuminating your path, you'll be pulled in the direction of your dreams. By lifting someone else, you'll affirm your confidence in the path you've taken and be someone else's mentor. Lastly, by being a part of a community of people like yourself, you'll have devil's advocates, number one fans, and a drive for understanding all under one roof.

Life provides some amazing moments. One of these is when someone takes the time out of their day to help us. Another is when we do the same and guide someone else.

Most of the time though, we are surrounded by people of similar skill sets, or levels of success. We call this group our peers.

This is the true spice of life. It's in the ability to lead, be led, and participate in something bigger than we are on our own.

Find a mentor who can help you be the best you. Join a community of people who challenge you to be better. And most importantly, be available for the person who looks up to you.

December 28ᵗʰ

Do your best to maintain a normal sleep schedule, even on weekends. The variety in a personal trainer's schedule in conjunction with our weekend desires to go out and have fun, enjoy our social lives, and be "normal" can hold us back from feeling and doing our best. Our body responds well to consistency, so be sure to get your rest when you are off the clock.

The weekend is one of the most joyous times for modern-day humans. After a long week of work, you find yourself with an open canvas of time to live your life.

You can attend shows, go out to dinner, have drinks with friends, or simply lie on the couch and watch movies until Monday returns. This freedom is powerful.

But with great power comes great responsibility. You must remember that your body loves routine. Your sleep cycle is optimized when you go to bed and wake up within an hour of your normal time. No matter what you do with your time on weekends, do your best to go to bed at a regular hour and wake up near the time you would wake during the work week.

Your mind and body will thank you.

December 29th

Know the difference between caffeine-fueled energy and that of a good night's sleep. A cup of coffee is a morning delight and a great way to jump-start your day. However, cups four and five might be a sign that you are under-slept, dehydrated, or need better nutrition. Remember, you must take care of yourself to truly help others.

Energy drinks are everywhere. Coffee is the most consumed beverage in the world. Our love of caffeine is at an all-time high, and for good reason: it works.

Still, caffeine should not be a replacement for a healthy sleep schedule. Getting to bed at a reasonable hour and ensuring that you get at least six hours of sleep is critical to your success. Hopefully, you get closer to eight most nights.

Avoid the cycle that starts when you have a poor night of sleep, consume caffeine all day, and have another poor night of sleep. This cycle can wreak havoc on your body and make it tremendously difficult to feel good and do well each day.

There is nothing wrong with a little boost before a workout or that morning cup to get your brain going though, so enjoy responsibly.

December 30th

Donate some time to charity to realign yourself with the value of effort. When you get used to charging for an hour of your time, it can eventually lead to a sense of ego and entitlement when it comes to your work. We all need to make a living, but we must never forget our duty to serve the greater good. Give back and smile.

One of the most rewarding experiences in life is giving your time to charity. The hours spent doing something for someone else without expecting anything in return is good for the soul and great for your attitude.

Sadly, most people treat charity as though it were a bill due each month: they just pay it. There is certainly value to financial charity, but the most impactful is the gift of your time.

As trainers, we can be especially influenced by giving our time to charity. We usually charge for our time, creating a practice that can affect how we value our hours. We might begin measuring the worth of something by how much money we'd make if we were at work.

This is an unhealthy way to think, and charity work can do wonders to rid us of that mess while using our efforts to better someone else's life.

December 31st

Ask yourself what you really want out of this career on a regular basis. Some people are more than happy to do a certain number of sessions, help their clients, pay their own bills, and make it through life. Others want to teach mega-group classes, write books, design apps, train online, build brands, or come just short of conquering the world.

Make sure that everything you do in life is done in earnest and is true to you, your goals, and your ethics.

You'll meet thousands of people in your career as a personal trainer, each with their own set of goals and expectations in life. In time, you'll learn that some people value freedom more than money while others will do anything to have a few more dollars in their pocket.

Every few months, be sure to take inventory of your life and ensure that everything you are doing honors your original intentions. Your goals may change and your path may vary, but your ethics and heart should remain true.

Set your goals and run your race. It's all that you can do. It is all that any of us can do.

Day by Day

Acknowledgments

This book is the culmination of my life's work up to this point. After almost twenty-thousand hours of personal training and teaching in gyms, a decade of studying, and all of the thoughts and dreams about how I could help the world, I've arrived here at this moment, this book.

I would like to thank everyone who ever believed in me. Your undying love and faith make me feel warm on even the coldest and loneliest days. No matter how much my "me against the world" mentality drove me during the day, it was your unwavering support that helped me sleep at night.

Some special attention belongs to my parents, Nancy and Kevin Mullins Sr., for raising me to be a blue-collared worker with a white-collared education and a lover's heart. I love you both and hope that I've made you proud. My father's near-thirty years of military experience and my mother's tireless commitment to family and love are some of my greatest inspirations in life. You shaped this course long before the boat hit the water.

To Dr. Paul Bauer, Sean Hanrahan, and Jerome Winston: each of you men has in some way helped me grow up and become the man I want to be. One helped me eschew childishness in college, another helped me align my passion with a drive to help others more than myself, and the last has helped me conquer my fears and anxieties of life, love, and my pursuit to be the type of man that I've always aspired to become. Each of you men are guiding lights in a world of Sirens.

To my best friend, Whitney Kling, you are the love of my life and the reason that I'll push myself beyond what is comfortable. It is you,

Day by Day

and our future, that drives me. Your support of me during the long, arduous process of this book will never be forgotten as we continue to grow and help the world be a better place, together. I love you.

Thank you to Equinox and the Sports Club/LA for providing me with a place to help others, cultivate my skills, and grow as a man. While the commercial gym scene gets a bad rap amongst industry professionals, where else could I have fostered such growth and experience in only a decade? The relationships I've built, the clients I've trained, and the highest and lowest points in my career have shared a common home on 22nd and M street in NW Washington D.C.

To all my clients: thank you for the opportunity to guide you, your body, and your mind. It is a big leap of faith to invest in a personal trainer, especially one with the ego and fire that younger me once possessed. Your investment in me I hope has never felt wasted. I assure each of you that I always put your needs above my own and hope that you know how much I appreciate the hours we've spent in the gym together.

To my business partner and friend, Michael Pepi, thank you for jumping into the fray and building an epic project with me. We are going to do great things with the Daily Trainer brand and make the personal training industry a better place.

To the team at Men's Health, thank you for finding me when I was still figuring it all out. I'll always remember David Jack, Adam Campbell, and BJ Gaddour say yes to my audition for Next Top Trainer. That opportunity changed my life forever.

To everyone who is holding this book: thank you for wanting to be better and for trusting me to get you there. I truly think you are holding one of the best tools you'll encounter in your career. Maybe there will be another iteration down the line, but I can say with unwavering confidence that I've put everything I've learned in this book.

Day by Day

Lastly, to anyone out there afraid to take that leap, don't be. For the person who is used to never coming in first– you haven't found your stage yet, just hold on. To the ones who don't "fit in," great! Stand out in your own way.

We are all capable of great works if we believe in ourselves, trust the universe, and never stop trying.

About the Author

Kevin Mullins, CSCS, is a Master Instructor, personal trainer, and group exercise coach of ten years for Equinox. He has a degree in Kinesiology from the University of Maryland and holds several recognized certifications.

Kevin has published a digital book, *Elite Program Design Concepts*, is a featured writer on PTontheNet and the PTDC, and has been featured in Men's Health, Women's Health, and the NSCA PT quarterly journal.

In addition to his work with the Daily Trainer Project, Kevin is currently a managing partner for FITTER consulting group, a business dedicated to building elite and profitable fitness experiences around the world. Learn more at Fittercg.com

Lastly, Kevin enjoys a good bourbon while watching sports or anything in the Marvel Universe. He is a fan of all music, dabbles with the guitar, and treasures the opportunity to make memories with those he loves. He shares his life with an incredible girlfriend in Washington, D.C.

You can learn more at KevinMullinsFitness.com